PAUL, THE MAN AND THE MYTH

PAUL, THE MAN
AND THE MYTH

A Study in the Authorship of Greek Prose

by

A. Q. Morton and James McLeman

HODDER AND STOUGHTON

PREFACE

IN our society today a person who could not read words, who is illiterate, would live under a great handicap. This fact is so obvious that it needs no emphasis. A person who cannot read figures, who is innumerate, lives under almost as great a handicap. This fact is only slowly becoming understood.

This book is an example of how the range of conventional literary criticism can be extended by mathematical analysis. There is nothing in the book which involves any calculation beyond the compass of an eleven-year-old child. But some of the arguments are statistical and not arithmetical and statistics is a field where ten per cent can sometimes be only insignificantly more than five per cent and sometimes very highly significantly more than five per cent. To get most out of this book the reader will have to put something into his reading, but the authors have tried to ensure that his reward will be worth the effort involved.

A new method is expounded in this book; it should receive a new criticism. As yet there has been little sign of a fresh critical approach. It has been argued that this study of the largely unconscious habits of Greek prose writers is credible only if we can show that John Dickson Carr wrote the detective stories of Carter Dickson, or establish some relation between the early and late works of Henry James, or show that Burns wrote two of his best known poems, or comment on the fact that someone has said there are two hundred possible definitions of an English sentence.

We can only point out that Dr W. C. Wake's pioneer paper on Greek sentence length distributions has been in print since 1957. During that time many objections have been offered, none by scholars who have counted a Greek sentence length distribution, all by those who have carefully avoided this exercise and any risk to their own prejudices.

In the long history of New Testament studies no work has ever been more open to criticism than the contents of this book. Not only is the principle of argument exactly described but examples are set out so that any reader may repeat, or extend, the work. Only by such repetition, on Greek prose, can it be verified or falsified.

It may be as well to say what this book is not. It is not a conventional scholarly survey of the Pauline literature. It is a brief exposition of an objective method of determining the authorship of the kind of Greek prose found in the Pauline Epistles. The book then sketches the fundamental changes in our view of Paul and his times which we believe are inescapable when the decision about authorship is made.

This book offers a unique opportunity for realising how little is known for certain about the first century of the Christian faith and encourages the search for fresh evidence to lighten our darkness. It would be tragic if the response were to be a salvage operation designed to rescue scholastic reputations and protect established positions. Ignorance is never removed by concealment or camouflage.

The opinions in this book are entirely the responsibility of the authors. We acknowledge, with gratitude, the assistance of Professor A. D. Booth and Dr Michael Levison, of Professor K. J. Dover, Professor E. G. Turner and Professor R. M. Grant, of C. B. Williams and Dr W. C. Wake, of the Rev. James Morton, of Mrs B. Hepburn and Mrs M. Riddler, of the Carnegie Trust for the Universities of Scotland and of the Royal Statistical Society who have allowed some tables to be reprinted from their journal. The late Professor G. H. C. Macgregor was the first, and for some time the only, supporter of this work. To him our debt is obvious.

A. Q. M.
J. M.

CONTENTS

General index follows the Tables

PART ONE

CHAPTER ONE

THE PROBLEM

THE thesis which forms the core of this book is that by statistical analysis it can be demonstrated that no more than five of the fourteen Epistles attributed to Paul can safely be regarded as his. They are Romans, I and II Corinthians, Galatians and Philemon. This thesis is entirely new and must run the gauntlet of critical examination by those who are competent to weigh the argument. This is exactly what is required.

By lectures and articles over the past three years both in this country and in America the general sense of the thesis has become known. It seems that before the stage of critical examination is reached, a good deal of resistance has to be expected from New Testament scholars who reject both the method and the conclusions on grounds which have nothing to do with the principles of scholarly research.

There is little disposition among those whose training has been literary and theological to accept the possibility that what seems to them a purely literary and theological problem, the authorship of the Pauline Epistles, can be solved by means of statistical calculations. The attitude is well expressed in the reaction of one celebrated divine: "What a way to handle the Word of God!" One might as well say of the work of molecular biologists: "What a way to handle the human body!"

Again, the conclusions arrived at by this method run counter to the assumption on which most New Testament scholars have been working. As far as this question of authorship is concerned, they are content with a consensus of opinion which allows almost all the Epistles to be used as if they came from the hand of Paul.

The thesis, therefore, both in its method and in its conclusions, offers a stiff test to impartiality of judgment, especially to those who have written a good deal on the subject and may have to eat their words. To some, no amount of proof will ever be enough.

This part of the book is designed to provide the setting for this new approach to an old problem. It will show how the problem arises and emphasise the unsatisfactory nature of the compromise which has been accepted, *faute de mieux*, by all but a few New Testa-

ment scholars, historians and exegetes as well as theologians. The
first chapter simply states the problem.

In its most elementary form the question is: How many of the
fourteen letters ascribed to Paul in the New Testament are likely to
have been written by him? The emphasis here, of course, is not on
the method of composition but on the material as bearing the imprint
of one mind and that the mind of the apostle Paul.

It is assumed that material written by someone who admired the
apostle and assimilated some of his ideas, together with material
written by someone who wished his own work to be accepted as if
it had been written by the apostle, is to be distinguished from the
kind of material we desire to isolate. The theological importance of
this distinction, of course, will depend on the kind of authority attributed to the apostle as a formative influence in Christian theology.

To raise the question of authorship at all is to be prepared to admit
that the circumstances in which the New Testament documents were
written and preserved contain the possibility of genuine mistakes
about the identity of authors, and also of deliberate misrepresentation
of one kind or another. To what extent such errors, if they were made,
were blameworthy is a secondary consideration. But if they were to be
considered blameworthy or even reprehensible, this could not be
used as an argument against their having happened in connection
with the New Testament.

It is necessary at the start to disabuse our minds of modern ideas
of book production, authorship, copyright and plagiarism if we are
to understand the circumstances in which the New Testament took
its rise. Many of the literary practices now punishable by law were
normal behaviour among writers in the ancient world. Books did
not make money except for copyists. Book titles and authors' names
were minor matters. For example, "it has to be remembered that
title-pages were unknown, and that we do not know the name of the
author of any book of the Old Testament in the form it now has"
(H. H. Rowley). According to Roman Law, if a man wrote anything
on the paper or parchment of another, the writing was reckoned to
belong to the owner of the blank materials. The book was the
physical thing on which words were copied. It was the property not
of the man who expressed the thoughts but of the rightful owner of
the article.

In later Judaism it was a feature of some books that they were
intended to be received as records of what had been revealed to
some notable seer of a bygone age. They gained a certain status by
this pretended foresight. What was taking place in the writer's own
time is represented as having been foretold secretly by the person

whose name is given to the book. Who actually wrote the book was a question of no importance, involving neither fame nor royalties and referring more often to scribe than to author.

Again, certain types of literature were attributed to, and were intended to be thought of as uttered by persons distinguished in their lifetime for the appropriate abilities. Thus law issued from Moses, wisdom from Solomon, prophecy from Daniel.

Our concern here is simply with the fact of pseudonymity, but D. S. Russell gives an interesting section on the psychological presuppositions underlying the practice of pseudonymity in Jewish apocalyptic literature. He lists "corporate personality", the Hebrew sense of the "contemporaneity" of similar historical events, and the significance of the proper name as an "extension" of a man's personality. These factors predispose the writer of this type of literature to issue the work under the chosen name. Principal Russell concludes: "Such an explanation of pseudonymity, based on an understanding of Apocalyptic 'psychology', exonerates these writers from the charge either of deception or of delusion and indicates that behind the acceptance of this particular literary convention there may well have lain a genuine sense of tradition and inspiration in and through which they saw themselves and their literature to be in the true Old Testament succession" (*The Method and Message of Jewish Apocalyptic*, pp. 127–139, S.C.M. Press, 1964).

Few famous men in antiquity have been responsible for all the works attributed to them. This is true of Isaiah, Plato, Philo, Aristotle, Hippocrates and many others. The "Platonic Canon" includes seventeen dialogues now regarded as spurious, together with the "Definitions" which were so regarded even in antiquity. Of the writings under Aristotle's name "it is certain that many of those attributed to him are not genuine". Thirty-five speeches of Lysias exist, some doubtful. But 127 more are known from fragments or titles. In the Augustan age 425 works were attributed to him, of which more than two hundred were allowed to be genuine. Of Isocrates twenty-one speeches and nine letters survive. Sixty were known to Dionysius of which he regarded twenty-five as genuine. The Lamprias catalogue contains 227 works of Plutarch—"some of very doubtful genuineness".

Pseudonymous writings were abundant in the intertestamental period and persisted into the second and third centuries of our era. Referring to Epistles and Acts which purported to be by apostles or their companions, H. J. Cadbury says that they "would endeavour to suggest verisimilitude by using the content of the earlier literature for details. It is this tendency, of course, which makes it so difficult

B

to distinguish what is genuine and early and what is imitative and late . . . The Jews of the period had long practised it [pseudonymity] and it was not unknown to the Gentiles . . . Not only were apostolic names conferred by posterity on anonymous writings, but Christians of the second century and later generations deliberately and with good conscience composed books in the name of one or all of the apostles" (*Interpreter's Bible*, Vol. 7, p. 36).

Not everyone would be prepared to be as charitable about the motives involved in this kind of operation as Cadbury is when he uses the phrase "with good conscience". A careful scholar such as G. Milligan, writing about II Thessalonians, says he dislikes the word "forgery" and adds, "But I know no other word that brings out as well the deliberate attempt of one man to use the name and authority of another in his writing. In view of 3: 17, 18, there can be no talk here of a harmless pseudonymous writing" (Exp. VI, lx, p. 449n).

The conception of authorship is therefore far removed both in practice and in importance from the present day. Authors had no hesitation in making their books out of those of others, on the principle no doubt that what was good in their eyes was worth copying into their own book. "If my subject," says the younger Pliny (Ep. v. 8), "is an ancient period already discussed by others, my material will be ready at hand." We know that all the major books of the New Testament were made on this principle. The Gospels, Acts and Revelation are compiled rather than composed. The use of Mark by Matthew and Luke provides an excellent instance of the method. Some of the minor books show the same unconcern about what we today would call plagiarism. We need only mention the relation between Ephesians and Colossians and between II Peter and Jude.

This carelessness about the identity and prerogatives of authors in the New Testament period is one source of our problem. It raises a question that had no significance at the time comparable to the importance attaching to it in the context of modern historical scholarship. A document was valued for its contents in relation to the needs of the time, irrespective of its provenance. At a later period, it came to be valued for its authorship insofar as this was believed to guarantee the trustworthiness of the contents. Sometimes the value placed on its contents influenced the conclusion as to who could have been the author, as in the case of the Epistle to the Hebrews.

In such circumstances it is not legitimate to apply our modern canons regarding authorship and plagiarism without more ado. As Cadbury says, this was done on occasion "with good conscience".

At the same time deliberate misrepresentation is not ruled out. We are not justified in concluding out of hand that pseudonymity, either with good intention or without, is not possible in the case of documents later bound together to form the New Testament. The probability lies in the opposite direction.

The extent to which the end justified the means in book production in the ancient world went far beyond pseudonymity. One authority writes that "it was no uncommon thing in some early Christian circles to have recourse to fictitious narratives for the purpose of safeguarding the interests of the faith. Men, in whom the historical conscience was feeble, were easily persuaded that events necessary to establish beliefs which they firmly held *must* have happened, and from that it was a short step to the statement that they had actually occurred".

The point is amply demonstrated from those Gospels and Acts which were not included in the New Testament. It is a nice point to what degree it could be illustrated from the canonical Gospels and Acts. Certainly they did not escape the tendency. If the end is all important and there is little ability or desire to scrutinise the means, the door is open to many kinds of inventiveness. Nothing in the literary habits of the age would forbid an author to invoke the authority of an apostle through inditing a letter in his name. The fact that the church might later include the document within its canon in full assurance that its doctrine and intention were apostolic, is without prejudice to the question as to its real author.

Valid conclusions about an author's beliefs and activities depend on our ability to distinguish what comes from the mind of the particular author from what has been attributed to him in error. In the circumstances we have been considering, this means we must begin the examination of our material from the position of caution. We cannot begin from a position of trust in a tradition that may have a vested interest in a particular conclusion. This means also that any chain of testimony about the authorship of documents in the New Testament is not valuable in proportion to the number of links in the chain.

> "*The captain told the cook, the cook told the crew,*
> *The crew told me, so the story* must *be true.*"

Counting heads *pro* and *contra* in this matter is futile. Very often one writer has merely copied from another who copied from another; there is no evidence that the original statement was made by someone who had the means and acumen to arrive at a trustworthy conclusion.

We must be prepared therefore to find that there is no safeguard against the liability to be mistaken about the authorship of New Testament books. Initially this kind of question and the critical ability to answer it was wanting. Later on when the question did arise, the church had powerful reasons for preferring its traditional uncritical opinion. It is often tacitly assumed that members of the church in the second and third centuries were more scrupulous and less gullible in these matters than the generality of men. Evidence of this is difficult to find.

In general, though they are often reluctant to draw the obvious conclusions, New Testament scholars of today admit that these are the circumstances in which the New Testament came into being. The four Gospels are known by names of men who may have had something to do with the material they each contain, but are unlikely to be the authors or compilers of the books as they stand. The names themselves add nothing to our knowledge, since practically nothing is known of the people they represent. The Gospels might as well be numbered as named.

The same is true of most of the New Testament. The safest statement to be made about authorship and the New Testament is that the names rarely signify authorship in the modern sense, the one important exception being those letters which may rightly be assigned to Paul. Many Gospels, Acts and Epistles bearing the names of apostles were in circulation. They did not qualify for inclusion in the New Testament. They were certainly pseudonymous but the likelihood is that they were excluded for other reasons.

One interesting example is the writing known as the Acts of Paul. We learn from Tertullian that this document was written by a presbyter in Asia Minor. When taxed with it he replied with disarming candour that he had written it "only from love of Paul". Nothing prevented others using the same kind of liberty to produce not a historical romance but, following the example of the apostle himself, an epistle in his style and name. They could justify themselves in the same guileless fashion if need be. For that matter, when the Fourth Gospel puts words on the lips of Jesus which could not have been *ipsissima verba*, part of the writer's motivation may have been of this kind.

Pseudepigraphy was used by admirers as a means of prolonging or reinforcing the influence of a revered teacher. The more highly he was esteemed, the more likely was this to occur. The fact that documents are bound up together and profess to be by a well-known figure is no guarantee of total genuineness. The likelihood is rather that at least some are spurious. In particular, it is naïve not to consider that some time after Paul's death, disciples would wish to enlist his authority in a situation other than that in which he lived and should do so by issuing documents expressing Paul's putative views.

For example, an argument that the call to unity in the post-apostolic church was given urgency and apostolic warrant through the document we know as Ephesians, is not to be dismissed as ludicrous. Again, when it was necessary in the first half of the second century to refute Gnostic views, it is not fantastic to consider whether the Pastorals were designed to do this with the help of statements modelled on the genuine letters of Paul. Indeed, a little later (*c.* 170) a third Epistle to the Corinthians was written with this very purpose. It was highly regarded in many churches and Ephraem Syrus (360) treated it as a genuine letter by Paul.

It is evident, therefore, that if we wish to enquire into the beliefs and opinions of a writer belonging to the New Testament age, we have an imperative duty to guard against accepting as his, words and thoughts which have come from elsewhere, whatever the motive.

The nonchalant disregard for what we would call strict honesty and accuracy survived long after the early centuries of Christianity. A particularly affecting instance is that of the ninth-century Bishop of Ravenna engaged on historical biography. He confessed with unalloyed frankness: "Where I have not found any history of any of these bishops, and have not been able by conversation with aged men, or inspection of monuments, or from any other authentic source, to obtain information concerning them, in order that there might not be a break in the series, I have composed the life myself, with the help of God and the prayers of the brethren."

There is not the slightest suspicion of any malicious intent, but if we are interested in anything other than the personality of this charming man, we should be mistaken in placing too much reliance on his history. Perhaps the same might be said of those who were anxious that there should be no gap in the story of Jesus prior to his appearance for baptism at Jordan.

We can now take a second look at the specific question before us: How many of the New Testament letters were written by Paul? It is plain we have to reckon with authors who may have intended, whether with good conscience or otherwise, that their own work should be accepted as if it were from Paul. They may not have hesitated to adopt means to achieve success in this. In addition, we may have to reckon with third parties who, for whatever reasons, were prepared to accept writings as coming from the apostle without solid critical grounds for so doing. This is simply to take account of the ethos of that era as far as authorship is concerned.

The evidence is that Paul was a letter-writer. Fourteen letters within the New Testament have come to bear his name. The question is: In view of the possibilities which make it at least probable that the

collection includes some not from his hand, how are we to discrimin-
ate? What tools are available for separating the genuine from the
spurious?

During many centuries the church had no reason to ask this kind
of question. It was content to regard the New Testament as a
canonical book on assumptions which gave weight to other considerations than authorship in modern terms. A more accurate
knowledge, not only of Paul but of the origins of Christianity itself,
required that this difficult problem should be tackled. For more than
a century and a half it has been before the minds of New Testament
scholars. They have done their best with the tools at their disposal.

The fact that no possible division of the fourteen Epistles into
genuine and spurious could secure the approval of the majority of
scholars is evidence that the tools used for the purpose up to the
present have been unserviceable. It is possible to find scholars who
have accepted none, four and every number up to thirteen in various
permutations, Hebrews being abandoned by most as a lost cause.

Thus, to give examples, Edward Evanson at the end of the eight-
eenth century regarded Romans, Ephesians, Colossians, Philippians,
Titus, Philemon and Hebrews as spurious. Bruno Bauer and Van
Manen believed that all the Pauline Epistles belong to a post-
apostolic period. F. C. Baur held that we can be certain of Paul's
authorship only in the case of the first four, Romans, I and II,
Corinthians and Galatians, the "Hauptbriefe". Albert Schweitzer
accepted these plus I Thessalonians and Philippians. M. Dibelius
adds to this list II Thessalonians, Colossians and Philemon. A great
many omit only the Pastorals and Hebrews, for instance, Burkitt,
Rawlinson, Dodd and E. F. Scott. A minority includes the Pastorals
as "the posthumous recension of a number of *disjecta membra* of
Paul's correspondence (especially with Timothy and Titus) and
other fragments" (F. F. Bruce).

It is not necessary to draw invidious distinctions between scholars
who arrive at different conclusions on this matter. The simple fact
is as already stated. They have been working with instruments which
are not precise enough to execute this difficult operation. They have
done the best they could in the circumstances but it is unsatisfactory.
If it should turn out that some of them have come close to the truth
(and this is certain since between them they exhaust all possible
answers), it is not because these have used a sharp instrument or
used it better than other scholars. They have made a fortuitous
guess on the basis of other considerations than those of critical
analysis of the Epistles.

Hitherto no adequate critical method has been found which is of

general application to such problems. Conclusions on the subject
have been arrived at by *ad hoc* means and intuitive decisions, by
guess and by God rather than by navigation.

If this seems a sweeping statement, let us now look at the means so
far used for dealing with the problem of authorship. We shall find
that they necessarily involve so large a margin of error that they are
quite unreliable and inconclusive, except in the most elementary
instances. This means that where a great deal depends on the
answer, the ordinary methods of discrimination are least effective.
Literary and theological criticism do not add up to more than a
matter of opinion in the case of the Pauline letters.

CHAPTER TWO

LITERARY ANALYSIS

THE art of literary criticism increases our appreciation and enjoyment of the vast resources of literature. In this chapter we are not concerned to enlarge on this but to ask with particular reference to the Pauline Corpus whether literary analysis can help to solve problems of authorship and, if so, with what degree of reliability.

The theory was first proposed seriously by C. H. Weisse more than a hundred years ago. He argued that Paul had a distinctive style which is represented in its quintessence in I Corinthians. This Epistle can therefore be used as a touchstone and by this means it is discovered (Weisse maintained) that only II Corinthians, I Thessalonians and Philemon display the same purity, while Romans, Galatians, Philippians and Colossians have undoubtedly been debased by interpolation and redaction.

Weisse's method and conclusions were rejected but his importance lies in his notion that literary style might provide a thumb-print of authorship if it could be expertly exploited. This notion has remained as a mirage before the minds of scholars ever since. While it has never been regarded as sufficient on its own to decide issues of authorship, writers on the Epistles have generally referred to literary criteria in making their own case for the genuineness or otherwise of particular Epistles.

This chapter will show that the kind of use which has been made of the study of Pauline literature from this point of view has been disastrous. It has remained a matter of subjective preferences and has generally been taken up for the purpose of providing auxiliary support for a case already decided in the writer's mind on other grounds. In short, most ostensible literary criticism of Paul's letters is simply a form of special pleading as distinct from a scientific application of recognised principles.

J. Middleton Murry once said that any passage of Shakespeare, if long enough for a critic to feel its influence, could never be mistaken for a passage by Webster. This seems to be a simple statement of fact. If it means that a man's literary characteristics are distinctive of himself it is doubtless true. But if it means that literary men have discovered the principles on which nice distinctions may be made between one man's literary habits and another's, the claim is boastful.

Undoubtedly when the differences between the work of two writers are vast and obvious, the critic will have no difficulty in indicating these. But where they are minute or where there has been deliberate imitation, that is to say, where the ability to distinguish is most required, the critic will find himself progressively less able to arrive at a conclusion which carries conviction.

If, for example, he were confronted by two pieces of prose abstracted, without his knowledge, from Bunyan and Macaulay, he might say with great assurance that they were by two different authors. He might even be able to name them. But if two passages from Steele and Addison were presented, he might find difficulty in saying with any confidence that they were by two different authors and an equally skilled critic might disagree with him whatever his opinion. His uncertainty would obviously be highly increased if one passage given him was a clever parody of the style of the other.

If Macpherson and Chatterton had lived in a different age or had not been available for questioning we might still be arguing about the authorship of their forgeries. The controversies about who wrote Shakespeare's works are still with us. At the moment learned authorities are divided as to whether an important source for Anglo-Saxon history, *The Life of Alfred*, was written by his contemporary, Asser, or by some eleventh-century chronicler like Leofric, Bishop of Exeter. (See V. H. Galbraith's essay on "Who wrote Asser's Life of Alfred?" in his *Introduction to the Study of History*.)

The point is that literary criteria, used for the purpose of assigning authorship, do not yield convincing results in cases where such results are most needed. Literary criticism, however widely interpreted, is a blunt and awkward instrument for this kind of job, too imprecise and subjective to be decisive.

It is needless to illustrate this in all departments of literary analysis at this time. What is proposed is that examples of the main lines on which scholars have proceeded should now be given. These involve chronological considerations such as may be used to confirm or destroy the likelihood of a particular work being by a particular writer, the examination of vocabulary with the same purpose in view, and the elusive factor generally called style.

It is understood of course that the literary case is cumulative. It must be possible to say that a document belongs to the right period, that the language is such as the particular author would use and that the style is recognisably his particular style. Each of these criteria is fraught with its own difficulties, particularly in cases where the wrongful assignment of authorship on other grounds is most likely to occur.

The following quotation from a book until recently recognised as authoritative in its own realm will illustrate the kind of argument frequently met with in New Testament studies. "The language of the (first) Epistle of Peter has been supposed to be inconsistent with the distinctive characteristics of the Apostle. Now, according to the most probable accounts, Clement was a follower of St Peter; and the tone of his Epistle agrees with that of his master in exhibiting the influence of St Paul. This influence extends to peculiarities of language. Sometimes Clement uses words found only in St Peter's Epistles: more frequently those common to St Peter and St Paul; while his verbal coincidences with St Paul are numerous and striking."

What amazes one about a passage like this is the sheer imprecision of the whole thing and the nonchalant way in which vast assumptions are used as if they were self-evident truths. What are the "distinctive characteristics" of Peter? This author has not taken the trouble to inform us of his own opinion on the matter, let alone show that they have been defined and are generally agreed.

The "most probable account" that Clement was a follower of Peter is given elsewhere in the book as a conclusion based on the authority of Irenaeus who wrote about a hundred years after Peter's death. Is it the most probable or the only or the most congenial to the author? Can it safely be taken as historical fact without more ado?

How does the writer assess the "tone" of Clement's Epistle so as to be able to come to the conclusion that it agrees with that of I Peter? How does he measure the influence of Paul? What peculiarities of language in two writings permit us to evaluate the influence of one on the other? How many words do passages of what length require to have in common before they can be said to prove what degree of intimacy of thought between two writers? What percentage would be required to prove forgery?

Turning now to our specific subject, it is the easiest thing in the world to show that this imprecision, this leap from bare unexamined possibility to bland assumption, vitiates all attempts to use literary methods to solve the authorship problems of the Pauline letters. The result is a congeries of opinion, each critic arriving at the conclusion favoured by himself for other reasons, because there are no agreed principles of procedure.

Let us begin with attempts to show that specific Epistles could have been written by Paul because they can be fitted into the particular writer's scheme of Paul's life. The fact is that generally agreed dates for incidents in Paul's life are practically non-existent. This gives large scope to those who wish to find a place within his life for the letter they are anxious to authenticate. But it is merely a question of exalting one possibility above the others and being more or less indifferent to the fact that other scholars have chosen other possibilities with just as much or as little reason.

Thus history and authorship are so intertwined and there is so much uncertainty surrounding both, that no result is capable of showing any better right to be accepted than the other. If Paul wrote a certain letter, then he was present at a particular time and place and did, knew, understood, etc., etc. Conversely, if Paul was present at such a time and place and did, knew, understood, etc., then it is likely he wrote a certain letter. The conditional clause makes every conclusion tentative and incapable of ever being anything more.

The instances of this kind of argument abound in introductions to the Epistles and in church histories. Thus, if Philemon was written from Rome, it contains evidence that Paul proposed to revisit Asia Minor before going elsewhere. The Pastorals imply a visit to Crete, Asia Minor, Macedonia and Epirus. What weight can be given to this as part of an argument in favour of the authenticity of Philemon or the Pastorals or both? This appears to be no handicap to drawing conclusions and then proceeding on the assumption that they amount to proof. Problematic history is made to support problematic authorship and vice versa.

In his recently published *A Commentary on the Pastoral Epistles*, Dr J. N. D. Kelly does not use the argument that the letters are Paul's because they bear his name. He says frankly that "the practice of publishing one's own works under the name of some personage of the past, was fashionable about the beginning of the era". But on other grounds he believes the letters are genuine and in face of the difficulty of finding a setting for the letters in the life of Paul he argues that Paul was acquitted before Caesar's tribunal and after his release engaged in missionary work in Spain (I Clement's reference to "the limits of the west") and elsewhere. Not a new argument and not impossible but would it occur if it were not necessary to support the genuineness of the Pastorals?

Paul's imprisonments used as material in the argument about authorship lead to many diverse conclusions. The "Captivity Epistles" (Philippians, Colossians, Ephesians, Philemon) are all assigned to an Ephesian imprisonment by G. S. Duncan, to a Roman by C. H. Dodd, to a Caesarean by L. Johnston. They and their followers accept the genuineness of all four letters. So does

P. N. Harrison, but he prefers Ephesus as the seat of writing for Colossians and Philemon and Rome for Philippians and Ephesians, while C. J. Cadoux allots Philippians to Ephesus and the others to Rome. All have to find room and circumstances in their chronology of the apostle's life for their preferences.

But this is not the end of it. There are those who accept Philippians as by Paul and reject the others and some who accept all the letters except Ephesians or Colossians or Philemon. They also must argue from circumstances and a chronology which support their case. It is difficult to see how anything more than surmise emerges from all this, or rather a host of surmises.

Again, if we start from the dating of Galatians, it is bound up with the North or South Galatian theory, with the trustworthiness of Acts and of Galatians, with whether Acts 15 has or has not the same reference as Galatians, with whether Paul's visits to Jerusalem in Galatians 1: 18 and 2: 1 correspond to those in Acts 9: 26 and 11: 30; and all these are matters of controversy. In the midst of so many variables, how can literary analysis make any contribution on intricate questions of authorship?

On the letter to the Philippians one commentator says: "The date of the Epistle must remain uncertain in view of the dispute as to its place of origin: and whatever theory is held on this point is subject to doubt." For all this he is absolutely certain it was written by Paul. Thus, on the one hand, to secure a place in the chronology of Paul's life is supposed to contribute something to an argument in favour of Paul's authorship, while on the other to be unable to find either a date or a place of origin is no barrier to asserting Paul's authorship. Heads I win, tails you lose.

The second matter to be taken up is vocabulary. Let it be clear that there is no intention to deny that the study of vocabulary is of great value and its contribution to exegesis must always be considerable. But we are interested solely in its use as a literary criterion for the differentiation of authorship in the Pauline Corpus.

We have already seen how one author uses vocabulary in his treatment of I Clement. "His verbal coincidences with St Paul are both numerous and striking." In support of this he gives a list of twelve words to be found in I Clement and in the thirteen Epistles he regards as Paul's. This seems to him sufficient evidence of Clement's familiarity with Paul's letters. He may or may not have been. How the degree of sufficiency is to be calculated is something our author never even mentions.

This rule-of-thumb use of vocabulary for the purpose of showing dependence of one author on another, or the familiarity of one author with the work of another, or the "characteristic usages" of a particular author, is to be encountered in most books on Paul's letters. In some cases the conclusions drawn may be correct but this is as likely to be due to a hunch as to any other factor. The instrument is not capable of doing the job any more than a foot rule can measure to thousandths of an inch.

Because this is so, the usual procedure is for the critic to accept the vocabulary test if it assists his case and to reject it if not. If the vocabularies of Romans and Galatians are fairly homogenous this is regarded as material in support of Paul's authorship of both. If Colossians shows a widely disparate vocabulary from that of Romans it can easily be argued that the apostle is free to modify his vocabulary, that *hapax legomena* are not so significant as was once thought, that any Epistle is too small to include the total vocabulary of the writer, even on one subject, that, in short, the vocabulary test is of no account.

There is no need for further examples in this vein. Most readers will be well aware that the lack of a methodology leaves the door wide open to sincere nonsense.

Once again, it may be true that an author's vocabulary is distinctive of himself. But when it is asked: How distinctive and how can this be measured so that his prose may be shown to be his and no one else's? it is obvious that so far the question has not been answered, if indeed it has been asked.

The final matter on which we promised to touch is that indeterminate thing called style in writing. The word has many meanings. For the ordinary purposes of literary criticism it may be enough to have some definition that leaves wide scope for variety of opinion and even in the end for *de gustibus non disputandum*.

But if style is to be used as an argument for authorship in the Pauline Corpus (as it often is), it ought to be asked what kind of thing is significant and for what reasons. Most of us believe that to some extent it is true that the style is the man himself. Where we run into trouble is in reducing this to a useful principle rather than a vague generalisation. So long as we are content to make judgments which have no other basis than our own faith in our own literary sense, style remains a matter of taste and affords no method of coming to grips with the problem of authorship.

For this reason the stupidest kind of comment in any commentary is likely to be found in the section dealing with the author's style. An author, anxious to preserve Ephesians for Paul may (and did) write: "Ephesians may look like a compilation of Pauline phrases but if looked at as a whole it has a unity." So has a pile of stones, no matter what kind and by whom brought together—if looked at as a whole.

What is being conveyed when a writer on Philippians says that "the letter agrees in thought and language with the epistles which certainly belong to the Ephesian period" but "the old view that the epistle was sent from Rome is still by far the most probable"; nevertheless "the arguments against Rome are by no means unanswerable?"

E. F. Scott (in *Interpreter's Bible*, Vol. 11, p. 8) writes: "It may be confidently affirmed not only that the epistle (i.e. Philippians) is by Paul, but that it is one of the most characteristic of all his writings." What is the definition of characteristic? Philippians?

On the same letter F. W. Beare writes: "Philippians, which was also written from prison (Philippians 1: 7, 13–14, 17) is quite different in tone and content from these three" (i.e. Colossians, Ephesians, Philemon). How different? Since neither Scott nor Beare thinks it necessary to prove their statements we cannot know whether they are talking about the same thing.

Morton S. Estlin rejects II Thessalonians on grounds of style. The first Epistle is warm-hearted, full of personal feeling; the second cool and detached. What does he mean by style and may not the same man be both warm-hearted and cool, depending on the circumstances?

John Calvin was one of the first to perceive that the notion of secretarial interpolations might relieve the pressure when differences of "style" in books attributed to the same man seemed to endanger the canonical authority of a revered work. On II Peter he says: "I therefore lay it down that if the Epistle be deemed worthy of credit it proceeded from Peter, not that he wrote it himself, but that some one of his disciples at his command, included in it what the necessity of the times required." This cagey and imprecise statement is strictly designed to ward off the need to face the unwelcome possibility that the document might not carry with it the kind of apostolic authority which its inclusion in the canon is believed to imply.

Spitta was the first to introduce the idea that in the Pauline Corpus perceived differences in the "style" of the letters might be due to the use in some instances of an amanuensis. For example, he thought that II Thessalonians was probably written by Timothy. F. C. Burkitt on the other hand believed that both I and II Thessalonians were written by Silas with Paul's approval. (Incidentally, Harnack regarded both as genuine and written at the same time, the differences being accounted for by the fact that I Thessalonians was dispatched to the Gentile section of the church and II Thessalonians to the

Jewish. Kirsopp Lake agreed about destination but thought II Thessalonians was written later.)

On the matter of amanuensis a well-known scholar says of Philippians, "The epistle is written in the two names of 'Paul and Timotheus, the servants of Jesus Christ', but this does not imply that the younger man had any part in composing it, or even that he acted as Paul's secretary and wrote down what he dictated."

What is clear is that there is no agreement on what constitutes style for this particular purpose and we are in a wonderland in which each adopts his own criteria.

"They drew all manner of things—everything that begins with an M—."

"Why with an M?" said Alice.

"Why not?" said the March Hare.

Most pronouncements on style are no more than personal, subjective judgments to which other personal, subjective judgments may be opposed leaving it to be supposed that the only outlet for objectivity is the fatuous one of counting the heads on both sides and accepting the majority vote.

The situation is not due to the obtuseness of New Testament scholars, at least not altogether, but to the fact that they have had to use spectacles which are incapable of affording a sharp outline or to examine with the naked eye that which requires a powerful microscope for true definition.

In his famous commentary on Romans, C. H. Dodd refers to chapters 9–11 as probably "a sermon or tract on the subject of the Rejection of Israel which Paul had composed earlier". He continues: "Similarly, the discourse upon the universality of sin and retribution in 1: 18–3: 20 is different in style from the bulk of the epistle and seems to contemplate a much more definitely Jewish audience. Without having the marks of an independent composition, like 9–11, it seems to follow the lines of a sermon or sermons which Paul must often have had occasion to deliver." (*Romans*, p. xxx).

The author has detected some unspecified difference in style, occasion, audience. This is apparently a subjective judgment; it might nevertheless be valid. But how would it be proved? What is the style of Paul? How can we assess "the kind of sermon Paul must often have had occasion to deliver" with any degree of certainty?

Sanday and Headlam on the same letter in I.C.C. (p. lxi) compare Romans 3: 21–24 with Ephesians 3: 1–7 and comment: "The general tendency to the formation of periods on what we have called the 'telescopic' method—not conforming to a plan of structure deliberately adopted from the first but linking on clause to clause, each suggested by the last—runs through the whole of the first three chapters of Ephesians and has abundant analogues in Romans." They give eight examples from Romans. Does this prove that Ephesians and Romans are by the same author?

But they also detect differences between Romans and Ephesians which they attribute to three possible causes, with a view to maintaining their common authorship.

1. "The natural variation of style which comes from dealing with different subject matter." S. and H. take it for granted that there is a significant difference in what they call style but they offer no means of evaluating. What is it which varies when the same man is dealing with different subject matter? More important, what remains constant?

2. "The circumstances under which it [subject matter] is presented." Again, is there any proof that this affects style and, if so, how and to what extent?

3. "The special temperament of the Apostle." But how can we judge the special temperament of the apostle? Do we gather it from an initial assumption that all the Epistles are genuine and then use it to prove that this must be the case?

S. and H. give a fourth reason which we have already touched on, namely, the employment of different amanuenses. If a secretary is responsible for a significant alteration, can we still speak of the author as Paul?

It has been taken for granted by many scholars that literary analysis can give direction in our quest for some method of separating the genuine from the spurious in the Pauline Corpus. It must be obvious that the contribution of conventional literary analysis can never be uniform and conclusive. In most instances it is either useless or positively misleading. Helped along by not a little muddled thinking, this instrument is not the tool for the job.

CHAPTER THREE

THEOLOGICAL ANALYSIS

THE Christian theologian is not a speculative philosopher. He is very much concerned with what happened in history and is committed to setting out his conclusions about the relations between God, the world and men in the light of events which have their focus in the life of the historical Jesus. Consequently the records which are the intelligible source of evidence from which he informs himself about what really happened within the focal area are of cardinal importance. The obligation rests on him to use these written sources honestly. Questions of the authorship, provenance and reliability of documents are therefore fundamental to his aim.

While the theologian makes use of whatever methods are trustworthy for establishing the genuineness of New Testament documents, including literary analysis, his own particular instrument is the comparative study of theological tenets which the documents reveal. The development of an idea cannot take place before the birth of that idea. The disciple is not above or before but after his master. The Judaism of the Diaspora may have characteristics which differentiate it from the Judaism of Palestine. The theological ethos of Alexandria differs from that of Antioch or Rome. This kind of distinction can be used in formulating conclusions about the possible date and authorship of documents which come down without self-evident attestation.

The New Testament documents, however, present some singular difficulties in this respect. They are all fairly well attested as being in existence within a hundred years of the start of the movement and most of them probably within seventy years. This means that the time within which they were composed is very restricted. Consequently, any theological diversity is due rather to the internal ebullience of the movement than to evolution through the sheer span of time and space. It means that what is or is not possible as far as variety of opinion in any one writer is concerned is very hazardous to gauge.

The contrast between the Old Testament and the New Testament in this respect is obvious. The total Old Testament corpus stretches over centuries. The era of the eighth-century prophets, for example, is very well defined. The difference between pre-exilic and post-exilic thought in some respects is strikingly obvious. Consequently the chronological order of the Old Testament documents is broadly speaking, a matter on which a consensus of opinion is readily arrived at. There is very little likelihood that a book written in the time of the Seleucids will be attributed by scholars to an author who lived in the time of Sennacherib, though it is always possible that its pseudonymous author might belong to that era.

And yet, even in the Old Testament period, when the time-span is limited the difficulties increase. This can be seen, for instance, in the variety of opinion as to the date and authorship of Old Testament books preserved under the name of Isaiah.

If we start from a position of ignorance or with the possibility of pseudonymity of mind, the shorter the time-span within which various documents were written, the more difficult the question of authorship. Thus, if it can be shown that a work belongs to a different period from that in which the author of Romans lived, no question of common authorship can arise. Meantime it is still debated whether the author of Romans also wrote Ephesians since the possibility of near contemporaneity is not out of the question.

How nice and how valid are the distinctions of a theological nature which can be made between New Testament writings, and in particular those of the Pauline Corpus, and what weight can be given to these as instruments for discriminating between the genuine and the spurious?

An examination of the results of such theological analysis leads only to the conclusion that, for the particular purpose in which we are interested, it fails in the same way as literary analysis. It is least useful in those instances where results are most desired.

Theological acumen can tell us with reasonable certainty that II Peter is probably the latest document in the New Testament, but it cannot tell with any confidence whether II Thessalonians is from the same hand as wrote I Thessalonians and whether this in turn is by the author of Galatians. We are left to count heads and pick our winner and the general result has been that most of the Epistles attributed to Paul have been treated as genuine by most commentators.

The normal attitude of scholars is still that indicated by A. S. Peake when he asserted that the burden of proof lies on the assailant of authenticity. "A piece of literature bearing the name of a definite author and claiming to be his work, is assumed to be genuine unless some cogent reason to the contrary can be offered" (*Commentary*, p. 814).

This is an assumption which could be made only if we close our eyes to the facts of pseudonymity, of compilation, of the methods and motives leading to the collection of works into a corpus, of the dogmatic needs of apostolicity and of other factors which make it needful for every commentator to discuss the question of authorship.

The fact is that both from the point of view of the historical setting of the New Testament documents and from that of the question as to what is the range of any author's mind, we are in ignorance of the main criteria necessary for arriving at precise knowledge about the authorship of the books by means of theological analysis. The best that can be said is that in some cases the balance of probability inclines to common authorship, in others not. To go beyond this is to take a leap in the dark, which most commentators are not loath to do.

Chronology is the backbone of history. To know the sequence of some events is to have some clue as to what is possible in the reconstruction of the history. We can have some idea whether we are near the head or the tail of the animal. In the New Testament period many vertebrae are missing or cannot be placed with assurance. Thus, a table giving dates assigned to the principal events from the crucifixion to the death of Peter and Paul by four authorities, namely Harnack, Turner, Ramsay and Lightfoot, shows that in not one out of the eleven events listed do all four agree. Disparities range from one year to twenty-six years. More recent authorities agree no better.

From some points of view this is of little consequence, but in a theological analysis of the New Testament with a view to establishing authorship it is a serious handicap. It deprives the scholar of a very useful "before and after" time-reference which could, in certain circumstances, help to give a definite position within the New Testament era to at least some of the documents. This in turn would be of some help in placing others.

It is extremely difficult if not impossible to estimate in terms of time the growth and development of a theological opinion, if the objective scale of events is wanting. We are left to the caprice of our own subjective judgments of what is possible, as for instance whether the man who wrote Galatians could also entertain some of the ideas found in the Pastorals.

It is not surprising, therefore, that the authorship of the Pauline Corpus has been continuously debated. Controversy about exegesis and interpretation and about the possible range of an author's mind in the early Christian era is continuous. Those who wish to conserve as many of the letters as possible for Paul have only to refuse to admit that the apostle had limits to the compass of his ideas such as could be predicated of and detected in other writers. Those who concede that some of the letters were not by Paul have tentatively to suggest that this is unlikely to be the case. Usually it is a debate between what is sometimes called "the versatility of Paul's genius" and the improbability that he entertained certain notions or confronted certain circumstances.

The Pastorals show this debate going in favour of those who have doubts about Paul's authorship. The bones of contention are such as whether the heresies mentioned are later than Paul's time, whether the conception of faith in these Epistles is Paul's, whether the state of church organisation revealed in them is not later than Paul's era. Some have found a beloved compromise in this situation by concluding that the Epistles are not by Paul but they contain what are called "Pauline fragments".

Dr Kelly has recently refurbished the case for Paul's authorship. He finds himself obliged to use his casting vote rather often. The absence of the Pastorals from Marcion's canon and from the Chester-Beatty papyrus (P46) is considered fatal to this argument by many scholars. Dr Kelly takes the view that Marcion knew of their existence (of which there is no proof) but chose to omit them, not because he thought them spurious but because he was against their anti-heretical tone and their deference to the Old Testament. As regards P46 he believes, contrary to common opinion, that either the Pastorals may have been included in the complete codex or, if not, their exclusion is accounted for by the theory that the codex contained only Paul's church letters.

Dr Kelly believes that the false teaching referred to in the Pastorals could have arisen within Paul's lifetime. He concedes that there is a difference in "theological tone, perhaps also in theology" and that in the language and style they are "noticeably different from that of the acknowledged Paulines".

But he maintains that these letters are "an altogether different genre of Epistle" (does this mean any more than that they are different?). They deal with other subjects and are written by an older man. These facts are taken as a partial explanation, but Dr Kelly thinks the chief factor is Paul's use of an amanuensis. If, however, an amanuensis produced something so unlike what Paul himself would have given us, in what sense is the product Paul's?

When we turn to the "Captivity Epistles" the case is somewhat different. Many scholars are prepared to admit that Ephesians is not by Paul but "Pauline"; some have doubts about Colossians, but most regard it as genuine; while there is little disposition to question Philippians and Philemon.

It is in the case of these letters that the question of the range of Paul's mind assumes major importance. It is here also that it becomes most obvious that there can be no hope of agreement on such a matter simply because the question of authorship is prior to the question of the range of Paul's mind.

To try to settle any argument about what it was possible for Paul to think with a view to estimating whether he wrote a particular document or not, while at the same time using the particular document as evidence for the capacity of Paul's mind, is so obviously circular reasoning that it is futile. Nevertheless this is the kind of impasse in which theological analysis finds itself. Some scholars think nonetheless that in the end this can turn out to be an objective argument yielding assured results. If a scholar is wise and unbiased enough, his conclusions will be right.

But it is not only wisdom and lack of prejudice that are needed here. The conditions for a solution are not present; the technique is faulty. Theological perspicacity cannot discover evidence of the kind it needs to solve the problems of authorship. So long as it has no better method it will achieve no surer results. Over all its attempts to assign authorship will be written "perhaps".

This would seem to be patent from the fact that, using the same evidence, equally accomplished scholars can reach divergent conclusions. These matters have been debated intensely and over a long period. The prospect of even a consensus of opinion is no nearer.

Almost all theologians would admit that in Ephesians there are some ideas which are more fully developed than elsewhere. Some might even allow that new ideas not found in the other letters are present. Thus Paul's mission is pictured as being to make Gentiles fellow-heirs with the Jews, reconciliation is between Jew and Gentile, spiritual gifts are not imparted by the spirit to all believers but bestowed by the ascended Christ on special men, a descent to Hades is referred to whereas in other Epistles burial only, Paul classes himself with "holy apostles and prophets" who are the foundation of the faith whereas in other letters they and he are servants of Christ who is the only foundation.

These and similar points are taken on the one hand to be ideas which only Paul could have the spiritual insight to conceive and develop. On the other, they are thought to be evidence of a setting in the second generation of the church.

The relation between Colossians and Ephesians has been a source of difficulty in itself since the latter embodies a large proportion of the former. But Colossians also sets some problems as regards its theology. Thus F. W. Beare states that the Christological passage in

1: 15–20 has "no real parallel in any other letter". It has affinities with the Fourth Gospel and Hebrews. The emphasis has moved from the work of Christ to the person of Christ, from soteriology to cosmology. Many phrases common to other Epistles are not used; others bear a different significance.

Again the decision as to whether we have here the work of the man who wrote the earlier Epistles is left to subjective considerations as to what is possible to that necessarily indeterminate entity, the mind of Paul.

The same kind of considerations are present in reference to the famous passage in Philippians 2: 5–11. It is argued that only Paul could have arrived at such a sublime conception of the work of Christ. The same argument doubtless could have been used by those who attributed Hebrews to the apostle.

The difficulties in the relation between I and II Thessalonians have already been mentioned but here also some scholars have found that there is an incompatibility of view regarding the parousia. Is the end imminent and unannounced (I Thessalonians) or is it still to be preceded by some striking events which give ample warning (II Thessalonians)? Are both conceptions capable of being held simultaneously in one mind or must we conclude that they come from different minds, one or neither the mind of Paul?

The spread of theological opinion over the whole of the Pauline Corpus is remarkable in its diversity. One argument for dating Colossians and Ephesians some time later than Corinthians and Romans is "the apparent progress in Paul's thought of the church as the body of Christ" (F. F. Bruce). We may say that the range on this subject is from an association bound together by a common enthusiasm to a unity possessing a creed, an apostolate, a quasi-hierarchical polity.

Streeter, in his *Primitive Church*, has shown the diversity in different areas of the empire leading in due course to Ignatian episcopacy. But how far this could have proceeded by the time of Paul's death or in the mind of the apostle himself is certainly not clear enough for use to be made of it in deciding questions of authorship within the corpus.

Once again, in the matter of expecting the parousia, the span of development is not to be questioned—from the Corinthian letters to Ephesians. Of the latter A. E. J. Rawlinson wrote, "The eschatological outlook characteristic of early Paulism is here so transmuted as almost to have disappeared." Professor Munck says that "While he (Paul) continued in his latest epistles to await the Parousia, nevertheless his emphasis seems to have changed from the expectation of the end to the present reality of the redemption wrought by his Lord."

The "transmutation" mentioned by Rawlinson and the "changing of emphasis" noted by Munck refer to something that took place at least among some congregations of the primitive church as time passed and the end was delayed. Whether it reflects an activity in the mind of the apostle is not to be decided till it is certain that he wrote all the letters in which it is evident, and it certainly cannot be postulated as a criterion by which authorship of the Epistles may be decided.

The best that can be done through theological acumen is very far from yielding a firm basis for Paul's authorship of the majority of the letters attributed to him. This is not the fault of neglecting the problem or misuse of the kind of means available to theologians. It is due to the fact that literary and theological criticism are incapable of reaching firm conclusions on this kind of question. With the best will in the world the most skilled and erudite are able to offer no answer which is more than tentative. It is safe to say that the hope of going further by these means is dead. This of course does not prevent theologians from proceeding as if tentative assumption were as good as proven fact.

PART TWO

CHAPTER FOUR

THE PROBLEM OF AUTHORSHIP IN GREEK PROSE

A NEWCOMER to New Testament studies might find it strange that so much time is spent discussing the authorship of Epistles when most of the letters tell you who wrote them, but there are many reasons why the authorship of any piece of Greek prose is not to be accepted without a critical study of the supporting evidence. All of these reasons reflect the fact that authorship in the ancient world was not regarded as we look at it today, nor was it surrounded by any of our present legal rights or safeguards. The first Copyright Act, passed in Britain, dates from 1709, and gave an author the sole right to his own work for a period of fourteen years with a second period of fourteen years if he was still alive at the expiry of the first.

In the ancient world an author's name was freely used as soon as it had attained enough celebrity to make its use by other men profitable. Sometimes the motive for imposition was purely financial. Soon after Isocrates died his son complained that the booksellers were putting his father's name on any rubbish because the name sold the book. A point of some interest in this example is that the son was not sure what his own father had written, and in one instance, the forensic speeches, was quite wrong.

Sometimes the name was borrowed to give weight to opinions which would not be much read without it. A view of religion which would receive scant attention under the name of its author might be widely read with the name of Moses attached to it, thus the names of the great were borrowed to give their prestige and authority to the works of others.

A common practice was for the name of the head of an institution to appear on all the productions of his pupils. Hippocrates founded the medical school which bears his name but he cannot have written all of the seventy-four works which came out of the school bearing his name.

Yet another reason for treating any ancient attribution of authorship with reserve is the incurable optimism of the human race. The violin discovered in the attic is a Stradivarius, the picture in the potting shed is a Rembrandt, the Epistle from the cupboard is Pauline.

To these illustrations could be added many others, all showing in different ways the position of an author in the ancient world and all emphasising that the attributions of authorship which appear on pieces of Greek prose are not to be taken at their face value.

There are other reasons, no less weighty, for adopting a critical approach to the New Testament Epistles, which pertain, not to the status of authors in the first two centuries A.D., but to the integrity of the critics at the present time.

If you are dealing with the life of a man known mainly through his writings it is a matter of some importance to determine exactly what he did, and did not, write.

It would therefore seem reasonable to expect any book which dealt with the life and thought of the Apostle Paul to begin with a critical assessment of the Epistles, directed to establishing which are his writings and which are spurious. This expectation is not often honoured by New Testament scholars. Some ignore the question altogether and start to build their house from the roof down to the ground, hoping that the foundation will be there when it is needed. Some discuss the question of authorship and state their conclusions by telling you what other men have said upon the subject. It appears that they feel it would be impolite to thrust forward their own views and so they quote the weighty remarks of respectable authorities. The snag about this way of working is that each generation quotes the previous one as its authority and it is often impossible to trace the opinion back to its source and discover what evidence supported it when it was first put forward.

An alternative approach is to abdicate critical responsibility, even at the cost of integrity, and begin as one scholar has done, by introducing a study of the Colossians with the remark that no reputable scholar has ever questioned the authorship of this Epistle. This may tell us how the writer rates those colleagues of his who have doubted the Pauline authorship of Colossians but it contributes nothing to our knowledge of the Epistle.

This book does not quote any past or present authorities, for the simple reason that there is no case known to us of any scholar who has clearly set out what criteria he has used to make his judgment on which Pauline Epistles are by Paul and has then gone on to prove the efficacy of his criteria on a range of other works by a number of authors.

This book is an attempt to establish the authorship of the Pauline Epistles on an objective basis. There may be objections to the method and there may be errors in it but these must be demonstrated, and corrected, by an examination of Greek prose. The same techniques are applied to the Pauline Epistles as are applied to the works of Isocrates or Demosthenes.

It is customary, when discussing questions of authorship and of integrity, to take the evidence under two heads, the external evidence of history and tradition and the internal evidence supplied by an examination of the documents themselves.

For the Pauline Corpus—the name is used without prejudice, as the lawyers would say, as a reference to all fourteen Epistles from Romans to Hebrews which have at one time or another, or by one person or another, been attributed to the Apostle Paul—the external evidence is scanty. The Epistles must have all been written, if by Paul, before the end of the sixties (by which time Paul was dead) and before the first traces of them appear in I Clement; it is A.D. 135 before Marcion supplies indisputable evidence of their existence. About the gathering of the Epistles into a collection, nothing is known.

A quick judgment of the value of the external evidence can be made by looking at any of the standard introductions to the New Testament literature and there see laid out all the diverse interpretations of the evidence. It is clear that evidence which can be read in so many ways is not decisive. Equally this means that a decision must be made on the internal evidence. This in turn means that most reliance must be placed on stylistic evidence.

At once trouble looms ahead. The word "style" is used in so many senses that it has almost lost all meaning. But from here on this word "style" will be used in one restricted meaning, the choice of word by an author. For the purposes of this enquiry composition is understood to be the selection of one word from a number of alternatives and placing of that word in a phrase, a clause, or a sentence. And style is here used to denote the personal element in that choice.

There are many influences which bear upon the selection of words in the process of composition. It is obvious that the language being used determines the words we select. "The man shot the dog" is a very different statement from "The dog shot the man". The position of a word is important in writing English. These choices which depend on the language are the subject of the grammarians' study.

A deep and pervasive influence on the choice of word is subject matter. When a letter is written to the Romans on the subject of law, this not only means that words like "*nomos*" will be common in the letter, it also means that there are images and comparisons which are directly relevant for illustration or contrast, and also that there are other images and arguments which are totally irrelevant and will not appear in the letter. Though warnings about the influence of subject matter on style have been issued for long enough, the influence is still consistently under-estimated.

Another influence which bears upon our choice of word is the cultural background of our time. This has been happily illustrated by Geoffrey Gorer who points out that young American males are rewarded by a candy or a cookie but are punished by being sent supperless to bed. This practice has conditioned the vocabulary of compliments so that the grown man talks of the female in terms taken straight from the larder. He calls her "honey", "sugar", "sweetie pie", and will, when pressed for a special compliment, tell her that she looks "good enough to eat".

The influence of cultural background can be seen in the rise and fall of words. In English some words can be traced moving from the aristocracy down to the working class while other words, slang in particular, rise to respectability. An example of the movement of words can be seen in the use of diminutive nouns in the New Testament, for these were common in classical comedy but were not much used by those who aspired to write literature.

The last influence to bear upon the choice of word is the personal preference of the author and it is this influence which is of interest here. An author's personal preference is most easily examined in two places; in his choice of synonymous alternatives and in his use of common words.

In all languages there are pairs of words which have much the same meaning. In English, you find "scarcely" and "hardly"; "since" and "because". There is no great distinction of meaning between these words yet one author will tend to use "scarcely" much more often than he will use "hardly". This preference can be made the basis of a precise test of authorship where the works of dispute can be compared with some background material which is contemporaneous. The use of this kind of test is fully dealt with by Professor Alvar Ellegard in his two books, *Who was Junius?* (Almquist and Wiksell, Gothenburg, 1961) and *A Statistical Method for Determining Authorship*, (Gothenburg Studies in English, 1961).

In the circumstances of the Pauline Corpus there is restricted scope for this kind of test.

The second place to look for the author's personal habits is in his use of very common words. These are the words so commonly used that they are found in every subject and so are neutral for any subject.

The importance of these words and the neglect of them to which we are all accustomed can be shown by a simple example. Here is a piece of prose, actually Greek prose in translation.

First here are the six commonest words translated:

And he – – – – – – – – – and the – – – the – – – – the – – – – – – –.

Now here is the same text with only the six commonest words omitted:

– – said, there was a man who had two sons – – younger said to – father, Father, give me – share of property that falls to me.

In the first case it is quite impossible to tell the subject of the narrative, but in the second, though the elegance has suffered, the meaning is quite clear and the source can be identified. The passage is the start of the parable of the Prodigal Son in the Revised Standard Version.

The point of this illustration is that seven out of the twenty-two Greek words contribute little to the literary value of the prose but merely act as the bony skeleton which support it. The meaning and the quality of the prose depend on the fifteen rarer words. This generalisation is sound, that elegance, quality and literary content of prose depend on the rarer words, the essential organisational structure on some very common words. So true is this, that we all ignore these common words in normal reading and study, because the rarer words have so much more interest in them. But the frequent use of these filler words means that they tend to become habitual in use, and so a good subject for stylistic studies.

Habits are never completely rigid, so that a statement of the kind which says that every thousand words of Plato has forty-seven nouns must be nonsensical. It might be possible to say that any thousand words of Plato has, on the average, forty-seven nouns in it. As soon as you make a statement of this kind, about the average value of a variable quantity, you have begun to talk the language of statistics. Statistical techniques have been developed to give precision to just such statements about variable quantities.

To understand the role of statistical argument in the development of a test of authorship it is essential to grasp some simple principles which are not yet the normal equipment of literary scholars.

The first of these is the use of the probability scale. We all make judgments about the probability of an event though we often talk of it as likely or unlikely or use some phrase such as "all responsible critics are agreed that this is so". Usually we are trying to show that, of two alternatives, one is much to be preferred to the other.

Using a simple scale can remove much of the difficulty involved in such comparisons. At one end of the scale shown, we put events

which are quite certain to happen and for these we write the probability that they will occur as $p = 1$. At the other end of the scale
we put events which are quite certain not to happen, and for these
we write $p = 0$. (See figure.)

Now it must be admitted that there is no event which we can be
quite certain that it will happen but the probability that the sun will
rise tomorrow is so near to $p = 1$ that we can write $p = 1$ without
introducing appreciable error. Just so we can assess the probability
that you will fly to the moon on feather wings waved by your arms
as $p = 0$ without introducing error.

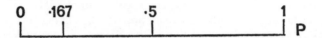

Between these two extremes we can place all other events. This
can be done either by argument from first principles or by experiment. If you toss a penny it will come down head or tail. Both are
equally likely and one or other is certain to happen so that the
probability of either is $p = 0.5$. In the same way a dice has six faces
and all have the same chance of turning up in one throw, so the
probability for any one face of showing in one throw is $p = \frac{1}{6} = 0.167$.

When you cannot deduce from first principles what the probability
of an event will be, an experiment will give an estimate of p. You can
toss a penny and count the heads and tails. Only rarely would one
hundred tosses give you exactly fifty heads and fifty tails but most
experiments will give a result near to this proportion and the estimate
derived from such an experiment can be used and refined by further
experiments. If you toss a penny one million times, the ratio of heads
to tails will lie very near to unity.

In this way the probability of an author using any particular word
can be assessed by using estimates based on other passages from his
works.

Before leaving the probability scale there is one point about its
use which cannot be over-stressed to students of literature. As any
event must either happen or not happen, the probability p that it will
occur, plus the probability q that it will not occur, always add to
unity, $p + q = 1$. This may seem to be labouring a truism but neglect
of this fact has ruined many literary investigations.

For example there has recently been published a paper which deals
with the occurrence of diminutive nouns of the Gospels. The results
are expressed as so many diminutive nouns per page of printed text.
Unless the number of nouns per printed page is about equal this

calculation is meaningless. The investigator goes on to argue that these nouns are commoner in one Gospel than in another because the first Gospel has a rate of twelve diminutive nouns per page and the second Gospel has eleven only per page. That this is a difference must be admitted but that it means anything has yet to be shown. An author who uses diminutive nouns at the rate of $11\frac{1}{2}$ per page is likely to write passages at the rate of twelve per page and also at the rate of eleven per page.

If the author of this unfortunate paper had set out his ideas clearly at the start of his work he could have established some valid conclusions. He would have had to record the number of nouns which are diminutives, say X, and then record the number of nouns which are not diminutive, say Y. The total number of nouns is $X + Y$ and the rate of using diminutives is $\dfrac{X}{X + Y}$. It might then have been obvious to him that he must show the rate of use in one Gospel is higher than the rate in the other and any textbook of statistics will show how to deal with this problem.

In any scientific work you will find the data not only inclusively defined but also exclusively defined. A statistician who talks of the number of people who die on a given day will always indicate what the other half of his equation is, the number of people who did not die on that day or the number who died on another day or the number who had been expected to die on that day.

No scientist will make such meaningless statements as—"the number of adjectives in the book is five hundred"—and leave you to guess what the background of the discussion is supposed to be.

That is why it is important not only to say what your data is but also what it is not.

To understand how a test of authorship can be devised and applied, it is necessary to grasp a second principle, which governs the relationship between a large group, called a population, and a smaller group, called a sample, drawn from the large group according to the rules for sampling.

Populations and samples are familiar to us, though not under these names. A common example is a hand of cards dealt out in a bridge game. Fifty-two cards are shuffled and each player gets a sample of thirteen. The hand dealt out to each player resembles the pack from which the cards have come for the very obvious reason that all the members of the hand are also members of the pack, but bridge hands also differ from each other because thirteen cards cannot fully represent fifty-two. In a hand of thirteen cards you

D

cannot have equal numbers of four suits, as you do have in the pack from which the hand has come.

The result is that we expect bridge hands to resemble each other because of their common origin, and yet to differ from each other because there are bound to be variations between hands. That is why no one would accuse a dealer of cheating just because one hand had no ace in it while the expectation is to find, on the average, one ace in a bridge hand. However, a hand which had five aces in it is one to which exception would rightly be taken.

This is about as far as commonsense argument will carry you; that there are differences between hands which need no other explanation than the fact that hands drawn from the same pack will vary and also that there are some differences which do require an explanation.

You might feel that, if you have not had a single ace dealt out in the course of a whole evening's bridge, a protest would be in order, but any suggestion that this does not happen among gentlemen needs to be supported by some mathematical analysis. Such an analysis might show that what had happened is very unlikely to have happened by chance and so another explanation is to be sought.

If you got a series of hands in a bridge contest which seemed to you to be peculiar and a statistician showed you that you might expect to meet such a run of hands, by the operation of chance alone, one evening every month, you would hesitate to challenge the integrity of the dealer. If the conclusion was that such a combination of hands was to be expected only once in nine hundred years of continuous play, most people would feel that some action was justified.

But in all this there is no certainty, only probability. Only some such occurrence as five aces coming from a pack completely justifies a charge of cheating. In all other cases you must act on probability and base your action on whether you accept the situation as one which is probable or improbable to have arisen by chance.

This is exactly the situation in literary analysis. There can never be any certain conclusion that any work was written, or not written, by any author: only a balance of probability for and against the assumption. One test indicates that the probability of Hebrews having been written by the author of Galatians as about 0.00012, about one chance in eight thousand. For all the odds against it, the proposition might still be true, but the scholar who accepts this and acts upon it has 7,999 chances of being wrong, to one chance of being right.

The relationship of the population and sample fixes the pattern of argument for a test of authorship. The basis of the test is that, in respect of the habit under examination, all the works of the author form a single population and any of his works can be regarded as samples drawn from this population.

The first step is to take some work by an author which is accepted as representative of his style and free from any suspicion of emendation. This work is divided into parts, perhaps quarters, and it has to be shown that, in respect of the habit under examination, all the parts of the work can be treated as samples drawn from the whole work. Any differences in the stylistic habit which exist between the parts of the work must be the kind of differences which one expects to find between samples drawn from a single population.

When this has been done for a selection of works, then all the works of the author are tested and again the purpose is to show that all differences between the works are no greater than sampling differences, so that all the works of the author can be treated as a single population from which any of his works, or parts of works, can be drawn as samples.

The third stage is to show that what is true of the first author who has been examined is also true of all the writers in the class which he belongs. In the case of the Apostle Paul, all writers of Greek prose. By doing this you show that you are dealing with general habits and not simply the personal habits of an individual.

The last step is to show that the tests are sensitive enough to be of practical value, and exclude from the population of an author's works any which he did not write. Of course no single test will exclude all the spurious works attached to an author's name. If we compared half a dozen habits in two different writers, it is likely that the men would resemble each other in some of the habits. This makes it necessary to evolve a battery of tests. Just as the police will specify half a dozen physical characteristics of any wanted man to enable him to be picked out from all the people who will resemble him in a few particulars, so literary identification should be based on a number of tests.

For a student of the Pauline Corpus the class of writer to be examined is that of writers of homogenous continuous Greek prose. It is hardly necessary to define "Greek" and "prose" but some other elements in the definition might be better of a little explanation.

"Continuous" is to ensure that samples are not made up from short prose insertions between dialogue or verse, nor of prose taken from fragmentary texts. The samples are blocks of prose taken as one piece.

"Homogenous" is used in its mathematical sense to ensure that all the data are of one kind. In literary studies it is applied to works in which all the parts of the work are consistent with each other and with the whole work. This implies that homogenous prose is made up and set down by one man. Homogenous prose is to be contrasted with heterogeneous prose in which work by more than one author has been incorporated. The letter written to the Galatians can be traced to the mind of one man but the Gospel of Matthew has had copied into it over ninety-five per cent of the text of the Gospel of Mark, thus making it heterogeneous.

It is not possible to examine all the writers of homogenous continuous Greek prose and so one must use a selection.

It was at this point that the late Professor G. H. C. Macgregor and the author departed from the normal routine of New Testament studies. We went to classical scholars and asked them to nominate a set of samples designed for this type of analysis. Stylistic habits may be affected by time, by change of subject matter, by cultural milieu, by any one of a number of influences. We therefore asked our classical colleagues to select a set of standard samples covering just these possibilities. The samples would range from simple narrative writers to complex and conscious stylists, they would include a variety of subjects and cover long periods of time. So enthusiastic was their co-operation that what had begun as a private conversation between Professor K. J. Dover and ourselves is now an official research project of the British Academy. This standard set of samples will be put on tape and made available for use by any scholar who has a hypothesis which he thinks will apply to writers of Greek prose. The standard samples will be a fair but searching test of any such hypothesis.

The final set of samples is not yet chosen but they will cover much the same authors as are used here. The basic list is made up of Herodotus and Thucydides, Demosthenes, Lysias and Isocrates, Plato, Aristotle, Xenophon and Plutarch with Diodorus Siculus. For the particular purpose of the Pauline Corpus these have been supplemented by Philo Judaeus, Josephus, Clement of Alexandria and the other Clement who wrote the two Epistles. The other New Testament Epistles which are large enough to furnish samples are also examined.

The result is to examine the tests of authorship over ranges of time, subject matter, style and literary form which are very much wider than can be encountered within the Pauline Corpus. The scholars who attribute the differences between the Epistle to the Galatians and the Epistle to the Ephesians to the time which intervened between the two compositions must explain why the sixty years over which Isocrates wrote did not affect his habits.

In summary we are to look at a representative selection of writers of Greek prose. In each of them we will look at some habits which can be numerically expressed and statistically treated. The aim is to show that, in respect of these habits, all the works of the writer can be shown to be samples drawn from a single and stable population. The examination of half a dozen habits should exclude from the population of genuine works any which are spurious just as half a dozen physical characteristics will enable a jury to decide if the accused was present at the scene of the crime or if some other man was involved.

The first suggestion that habits might be used for the scientific identification of authors was made in 1859 by Augustus de Morgan who was then Professor of Mathematics in University College, London. It is interesting to note that his suggestion, made in a letter to a friend, was that the dispute about the authorship of the Epistle to the Hebrews might be settled by an examination of word length. We all know the writer who prefers to use the long word and de Morgan sketched out a plan to look at the average length of word used by an author. The number of letters in each word in the text would be counted and the average length of word in the text established. If all the other Pauline letters had averages which lay near enough to be drawn from a single population and Hebrews lay outside the limits of this population, de Morgan argued that this would be a decisive contribution to the debate on the subject.

In fact de Morgan's plan differs only from the plan outlined above and carried out in this book by neglecting to examine a representative selection of Epistle writers.

Unfortunately the words we use depend on subject matter and so the length of word we use is affected by the subject on which we write. Word length is not to be relied on in the circumstances of the Pauline Corpus.

CHAPTER FIVE

SENTENCE LENGTH AS A TEST OF AUTHORSHIP

THE first successful attempt to establish a reliable test of authorship was made by Dr W. C. Wake. Wake was looking at one of the most difficult problems in Greek literature, the seventy-four works associated with the name of Hippocrates. Wake looked at a number of possible indicators of authorship and the best results came from sentence length. His pioneer paper was published as—W. C. Wake, Sentence Length Distributions of Greek Authors, *Journal of the Royal Society*, Series A, Part 3, 1957, Vol. 120, pp. 331–346.

Sentence length is an intelligent test to make. There is no obvious connection between the number of words in a sentence and the meaning of the words in the sentence. The sentences we write range from one word up to more than two hundred and so the test is likely to be a sensitive one. We are all aware of the difference between Herodotus and Thucydides and anyone describing the difference is almost certain to mention the long involved periods of the one and the simple narrative of the other. So sentence length looks like a stylistic habit.

Wake's procedure was exactly the one outlined above, testing the parts of works against each other to show that sections of a work differ from each other only by the negligible sampling differences, then extending the testing to all the works of an author and then to a selection of authors. Only then did he examine the questioned works of Hippocrates. Wake restricted himself to writers directly comparable with Hippocrates but he looked at a number of others for interest and included among these were the Pauline Epistles. So the first scientific determination of the authorship of these Epistles is due to Dr Wake.

Wake examined the whole pattern of a writer's sentence lengths. An obvious test was the average length of sentence, called by the statisticians the mean length to distinguish the arithmetic average, the only one most people are likely to meet, from other measures which statisticians use.

Two writers may have the same mean length of sentence but one may have written nothing very far from the mean while the other may have ranged widely. A large number of very short sentences can be balanced by a small number of extremely long sentences. In another case the numerous short ones could be balanced by a group of medium long sentences. In other words to examine the whole pattern of a writer's sentence lengths you need to look at much more than his mean length of sentence. Wake did all the necessary investigations and showed that there were five constants for each sample which were valuable. The first of these is the mean length and it is obtained from the total number of words in all the sentences divided by the number of sentences. The second constant of the distribution is the median. The median of a group is the central value, fifty per cent of the observations lie above the median and fifty per cent lie below it. The third constant is the first quartile, a measure of the short sentences and this is the value below which one quarter of the observations lie. The third quartile is the value below which three-quarters of the observations lie. The difference between the first and third quartiles is called the inter-quartile range and is a useful measure for the middle range of sentence lengths. The inter-quartile range can be obtained from the other two observations quite simply. The fifth constant is the ninth decile. Below the ninth decile lie ninety per cent of the observations. The ninth decile makes a sensitive measure of the proportion of really long sentences without running into the difficulties which can be caused by the occurrence of one or two isolated very long sentences.

Now in each case these constants could be used to work out the probability of two, or more, samples coming from a population but the work involved would be considerable. It is simpler to set limits in advance and this is done by using the standard errors of the constants. For constants which are normally distributed—a technical statement of some importance—the probability that sample values will lie more than two standard errors away from the population value is 0·05. For three standard errors the probability is about 0·003.

So if we accept three standard errors as our limits of significance then samples from the same population will lie between these limits about 299 times in three hundred trials. It must be remembered that we would conclude, one time in three hundred, that a difference is significant when it is only due to chance. In examining, as we are about to do, several hundred statistics, some samples of outlying values will be found which have been produced by chance alone. These can be detected simply because they are isolated. They occur in works which are otherwise regular. If the two samples are not drawn from the same population differences can be expected to show in more than one statistic and in more than one test. But this is something which can be made clear as we encounter instances.

To construct a sentence length distribution you first need a definition of a sentence. For our purpose, a sentence is the group of words which end with a full stop (.), a colon (·) or an interrogation mark (;). This may seem a curious definition to a grammarian but it is one which means that a text by one editor can be compared with the same text from another editor and the differences are negligible compared with sampling differences.

The original punctuation of Greek manuscripts was rudimentary and the puctuation of modern printed texts has been inserted by the editors. The main difference between editors lies in the use of the colon and the full stop. If these two marks are accepted as interchangeable the differences between editorial marking disappears. The important point is that two scholars working on the same text and counting two hundred sentences should be counting the same thing. This limited definition ensures that this is so.

Once a group of scholars objected strongly to this mechanical mauling of one of their respected conventions, so our colleague Dr Levison invented a new name for this kind of sentence. He called it a "Spon" and under this name it was entirely acceptable. If the reader is in the least worried about the grammatical connotation of the word "sentence" he can replace it with "Spon" from now on.

To prepare a sentence length distribution the number of words in all the sentences in the text is counted. It would be tedious to deal with every sentence on its own and so they are grouped. All the sentences with between one word and five words are put into group one, all the sentences with between six words and ten words are put into group two, and so on. In statistics a group of this kind is known as a cell, and in this case the cell interval is five words, that is, our cells are five words wide. When the counting is completed the first step is to draw up a table like Table 1, which sets out the sentence length distribution of the Epistle of James in the text of Souter.

The first thing to do is to calculate the mean length of sentence. From a look at Table 1 it would appear that the mean lies between ten words and fifteen words. The third column of the table is therefore centred on this estimated mean and each cell is numbered away from this estimate. The two cells which contain shorter sentences are numbered in negative units, all those which contain longer sentences are positively numbered.

From column three (x) is prepared column four (fx). To do this every pair of figures in columns two and three is multiplied together. There are thirty-four sentences in the cell minus two so the product is minus sixty-eight. The negative numbers are added, the total is minus 122 and so are the positive numbers which add to plus fifty-five. The difference between these numbers is sixty-seven and as the larger total is negative the result is minus sixty-seven. The mean length of sentence is the mean value for our estimate—thirteen words— which is the central value of cell three, less, for the result was minus, sixty-seven divided by the total number of sentences, 157, and then multiplied by five as the cell interval is five words wide.

$$\text{Mean length of sentence} = 13 - \frac{67 \times 5}{157} = 13 - 2 \cdot 15$$

$$= 10 \cdot 85 \text{ words per sentence.}$$

It may be of interest to note that the true mean, given by the total number of words in all the sentences divided by the total number of sentences is 11·1 words. As will be seen shortly, this difference is not important.

The next column in the table (fx^2) is obtained by multiplying all the figures of column four except the totals, by the figures of the third column once again. The product of two negative numbers is positive and so all the numbers add together and come to 345. This total 345 is divided by the number of sentences, the result is 2·198 and from this is subtracted the square of the difference in totals in column four, namely $\frac{67}{157}$ which is 0·182. The result is 2·016 and this is what is known as the variance. The square root of the variance, 1·42, is the standard deviation. The standard deviation divided by the square root of the number of sentences—the root of 157—which is 12·5, is the standard error of the mean, in this case 0·12. A point to watch is that this standard error is expressed in units of one cell interval so that to get the answer in words you must multiply by five, and the standard error is 0·60 words.

This means, as was stated before, that 299 times out of 300, this sample would come from a population which had a mean lying between 12·7 words, three standard errors above the sample mean of 10·9 words and 9·1 words, three standard errors below the sample mean. The wide range which the figures allow may well come as a surprise to literary minds.

The other constants and their standard errors are simply worked out. The median is the central value in 157, so it lies at 78·5. In-spection of the table shows that there are thirty-four sentences of five words or less,so the median lies between six and ten words. The whole cell of five words has fifty-four sentences in it, and the dif-ference between the median, 78·5, and the total at the cell boundary, thirty-four, is 44·5. So the median lies into the cell at a position $\frac{44·5 \times 5}{54} = 4·1$. So the median is $5 + 4·1 = 9·1$ words. The standard errors of the constants other than the mean were established by Wake. The standard error of the median is $\frac{\sqrt{(N)}}{2Y}$ where N is 157, the number of sentences in the sample, and Y is one-fifth of the total for the cell which contains the median six to ten words, and is fifty-four divided by five = 10·8. Thus the standard error of the median is $\frac{(157)}{2 \times 10·8} = 0·6.$

The other constants are worked out in exactly the same way.

*   *   *

THE STANDARD ERRORS OF THE CONSTANTS OF SENTENCE LENGTH DISTRIBUTIONS

In every case N is the number of sentences in the samples and Y is one-fifth of the frequency for the cell in which the constant falls, i.e. if a constant had the value of eleven, Y would be one-fifth of the number of sentences in the cell which contained eleven, the cell eleven to fifteen words.

Constant	*Standard Error*
1. Mean	$\dfrac{S.D.}{\sqrt{(N)}}$
2. Median	$\dfrac{\sqrt{(N)}}{2Y}$
3. First and third quartiles	$\dfrac{\sqrt{(3N)}}{4Y}$
4. Ninth decile	$\dfrac{3\sqrt{(N)}}{10Y}$

5. The standard error of the inter-quartile distance is the square root of the sum of the squares of the standard errors of the first and third quartiles.

*   *   *

This isolated Epistle has been no more than an example of how the distributions are counted and the constants of the distribution calculated.

There are a number of restrictions in the use of sentence length distributions. The first is that there is a minimum sample size. Authors tend to group short sentences together and to write a few long sentences in near succession. So a satisfactory sample of an average Greek prose writer must extend to about one hundred sentences.

Sentence length is not reliable for dialogue. Dialogue has a number of very short sentences, usually the expressions of assent or of dissent and if these are included the result is that the distribution has too many very short sentences. If these very short sentences are cut out, the distribution has too many long sentences. A further trouble is that, in most dialogues, the proportion of actual dialogue-exchanges to the prose narrative between the exchanges varies. Plato's Laws is an example of this changeable relationship. The first two hundred sentences of Book 1 contain a number of rapid exchanges expressed in very short sentences while Book 5 begins with continuous prose.

That sentence length distributions should not be used in dialogue was made clear by Wake. In the authors examined in this book two further reservations emerge; both would be excluded by the definition of continuous homogeneous prose, but these limitations are worth exploring.

The first exception is those works of Philo which are commentaries on books of the Old Testament. The case is much the same as in dialogue, for Philo quotes a short sentence from, say, Genesis, and then writes his comment upon it. Samples from the commentaries are consistent with each other but not with the continuous prose which Philo writes in free composition.

The second exception is the fragmentary books of Diodorus Siculus. Gaps in a text might affect sentence length distributions in a number of different ways. You could argue that into two gaps of the same size would fit either a few long sentences or a large number of short ones. Short sentences are commoner than really long sentences and so a text with lacunae might show a higher proportion of long sentences. But whatever position you care to argue from it is simpler to test an author. It will be seen that the sentence length distributions from the fragmentary books of Diodorus Siculus differ significantly from the complete books of the same author. It is interesting to note that for both dialogue and text with lacunae, the occurrence of common words is not affected.

Turning to sentence length distributions of representative authors, the first set to be examined is that for those for the Epistles of Clement (Table 2). I and II Clement are two second-century Epistles. Some optimistic scholars have argued that they cannot be from the same hand because I Clement contains the first clear references to

I Corinthians and to Romans, and is written in a time of trouble. They interpret this evidence as supporting a date about A.D. 95 for I Clement and must then argue that II Clement, which is undoubtedly later, must be by another author.

I Clement is just over four times as large as II Clement, so that I Clement yields four samples of 150 sentences and II Clement gives a single sample. The main purpose of displaying the two Epistles in detail is to illustrate how works are treated in sections before they are treated as units. It is hardly necessary to refer to the constants of the distributions, in all respects the constants of the samples from II Clement lie within two standard errors of the constants of the samples from I Clement. Comparison of the two Epistles is complicated by the prayer in I Clement, cap. 59–62.

The next pair of sentence length distributions (Table 3) are from the two longer works of Clement of Alexandria, again the text is the Loeb edition. The two can be regarded as samples from one population without difficulty.

The next two sets of sentence length distributions are from the great historians, Herodotus and Thucydides (Tables 4 and 5). In both cases the text is the Oxford Classical Test. These two writers not only offer a contrast in style but they represent a searching test of a stylistic method. They composed their works over a period, describing the events of nearly thirty years, and they revised portions from time to time. In each case the first two hundred sentences of each book of the history was taken as the sample.

In no instance is there any difficulty in treating the parts of the works as samples drawn from the whole work; all the constants lie within the range of three standard errors.

Anyone who works on the Pauline Epistles is familiar with the assertion that any conclusions reached by the study of Greek prose writers must be regarded with suspicion as Paul was a Jew writing in Greek. This, it is flatly asserted, must make a difference. No doubt it does make some differences in certain respects but the next set of sentence length distributions (Philo, Table 6), taken from the Loeb text, as were those of Diodorus Siculus (Table 7), show that there is no detectable difference as far as sentence length distributions are concerned.

Philo wrote until A.D. 50 and played a prominent role in Christian thought, for it is from him that Augustine borrowed some of his leading ideas.

The first six samples are from the single Loeb volume and from them no queries arise, but Philo also wrote commentaries and three samples were taken from his commentary on Genesis. They are successive blocks of two hundred sentences. The three samples are consistent with each other, but they are quite noticeably different from Philo's continuous prose. This does suggest that one could use sentence length distributions to compare commentaries but not to compare commentary with free compositions, a natural expectation.

Diodorus Siculus wrote a history of the world in forty books between 60 and 30 B.C. Like all historians of classical times, his subject matter ranged widely and dealt with a variety of cultures and climates. Only Books 1 to 5 of the history have been fully preserved and the first three samples are the first two hundred sentences from Books 1 and 2, in the Loeb text, with the second two hundred sentences from Book 1.

As has been mentioned earlier, the opportunity was taken to look at sentence length distributions in three fragmentary books of the history just to see what limitations might emerge.

The constants show significant differences, though not large ones. The mean for Book 1 is 26·4 and with a standard error of 1·0 this sample could come from a population with a mean as low as 23·4. Only Book 32 lies outside this limit and it has an upper limit of 23·2. The median of Book 22 lies outside the limit of three standard errors. Both the first and third quartiles of Books 21 and 22 lie outside the limits of three standard errors.

The conclusion is that lacunae cannot be neglected. An odd missing sentence can be disregarded but gaps of any size and number affect sampling and must be treated with reserve.

In work of this kind it is important to cover the whole career and corpus of at least one author, for this is a protection against making judgments which might apply only to particular periods in his writing life. There are three authors all of whose works have been tested. The first (Table 8) is Lysias, who was known to pseudo-Plutarch as the author of 233 genuine speeches and to whom had been attributed 435. The text is the Oxford Classical Text, also used for Demosthenes.

Only Work 2 has been widely questioned. Work 2 has its mean, median and third quartile, outside the range of three standard errors.

To most classical scholars the works of Demosthenes (Table 9) represent a rigorous test of stylistic method. Not only was he a cultivated and conscious stylist in his writing, but also he has an unparallelled range of genre. In the Oxford Classical Text, Demosthenes has sixty-one works. Of these eighteen have less than one hundred sentences and are not suitable for this test. Of the forty-three to which the test is applied a number are questioned. H. J. Rose (*A Handbook of Greek Literature*, Methuen, 1961), lists as not

Demosthenes, numbers 7, 10, 11, 12, 13, 17, 25, 26, 33, 34, 35, 40, 42, 43, 44, 46, 47, 48, 49, 50, 52, 53, 56, 58, 59, 60 and 61. To these Rose would add, as a personal judgment, 51. Thus there are eighteen questioned works among the forty-three examined.

The mean sentence length excludes 34, 40, 47, 48, 49, 50, 58, 59 and 61. The median excludes 23, 40, 48, 49, 59, and 61. The first quartile excludes 23, 40, 49, 50, 59 and 60. The third quartile excludes 40, 49, 50, 58 and 59. The ninth decile excludes 40, 44, 49, 50, 59 and 61.

Thus there are excluded from the population of Demosthenes' works eleven of the eighteen classed by Rose as spurious. The only work accepted by Rose as genuine and excluded by the test is Work 23. An inspection of this oration soon shows why this is so. From sentence seventy-five to sentence one hundred there is a remarkable run of very short sentences, of the twenty-five, sixteen are less than ten words. A look at the text reveals that at this point Demosthenes is quoting from a law. The editor of the Oxford Classical Text has put a high proportion of the short sentences, in whole or in part, in quotation marks. If these sentences are omitted from the sample, or replaced by the next twenty-five sentences, the sample is quite in order in all constants. Once again the exception has been shown to be a meaningful exception, for the prose is not homogeneous in this region.

The result is to show that all the homogeneous works of Demosthenes, written as they were over a period of about thirty-five years, can be regarded as samples from a single population.

Of the eighteen works thought by Rose to be spurious and large enough to test, eleven have been shown to come from another population.

The next author to be looked at is Isocrates (Table 10) whose works constitute the most searching test of a stylistic method. Not only is he the conscious and cultivated stylist who once boasted that he had written an entire work which contained no instance of hiatus, but also he wrote for an unparalleled period of sixty-three years between 402 B.C. and 338 B.C. His last work, Work 12, was begun in his ninety-fourth year, laid aside during a serious illness, then completed in his ninety-seventh year. An Epistle dates from the following year, 338 B.C., the last year of his life.

The first work in the Corpus, Work 1, the Demonicus, is not his. A few scholars have argued for a connection by making out that the work is a compendium which Isocrates edited. In any case the work is not Isocrates' homogeneous prose.

A point of interest is that there are references in ancient literature to only one genuine work of Isocrates which has not survived, and this exceptional situation shows the regard in which his work was held.

Of the eighteen works long enough to supply satisfactory samples, Work 1 is outside the limits of three standard errors in every constant.

An examination of means shows that Works 5 and 12 cannot be from the same population as Works 2, 17, 18 and 19.

The median values of Works 2 and 17 are not consistent with the value for Work 4; the third quartile offers a choice of either Work 4 or Works 2, 18 and 19; the ninth decile Work 4 or Work 17. Not all the sentence length distributions are from a single population. One might well expect to find some discrepancy in Work 12 which is affected, as the editor of the Loeb text says, by the onset of senility and interrupted by the serious illness of a nonagenarian, but the choice is between the two groups, Works 4, 5 and 12 against Works 2, 17, 18 and 19.

There are two possible explanations of the change in sentence length. Works 4, 5 and 12 are elaborate and cultivated orations while Works 16 to 21 are the early forensic speeches, the only ones written by Isocrates to be spoken rather than read and so informal that he disowned them in later years. The change in sentence length might be due to this contrast in literary form, or it might be due to the passage of time, for Works 5 and 12 are his last works while Works 16 to 21 are his first works.

The theory that time has been responsible for change in sentence length can be tested in two ways. The first is by making a regression analysis which is a general comparison of mean sentence length with time. The regression co-efficient is 0·093, meaning that there is a change of about 0·28 word in the average length of sentence per year. This value is not significantly different from zero, so that this effect could have been brought about by chance. This explanation is permissible but must be regarded as not proven.

Many of the works of Isocrates are dated by reference to another work, so that the date of one is given as a year or two after the issue of another. An alternative procedure is to rank the works in order of mean sentence length and in the order in which they were published. When this is done the rank correlation co-efficient, a measure of the agreement between sentence length and order of production is 0·51 and for the value of t for fifteen degrees of freedom is 2·30 which would be considered significant as $t = 2·13$ for $p = 0·05$.

So it would seem that the passage of time is a permissible explanation of the change in sentence length. It is not an unavoidable explanation for the passing years also bring the change in literary form.

Confronted with the choice of time or literary form as the cause of the differences in sentence length, scholars unanimously select the change in literary form. They expect epideictic works to show the elaboration which, in English literature, we connect with the prose of Milton or Sir Thomas Browne.

This explanation of the alteration in sentence length would be strengthened if Work 2 were also informal and it is interesting, in this connection, to note that in Work 15, the Antidosis, Isocrates refers to Work 2. Isocrates has just had extracts read out from work 4 and from Work 8 and then asks that extracts from Work 2 be read. He says, "It is not however composed in the same style as the extracts which have been read. For in them each part is always in accord and in logical connection with that which goes before; but in this, on the contrary, I detach one part from another, and breaking up the discourse, as it were, into what we call general heads, I strive to express in a few words each bit of counsel which I have to offer" (Antidosis 68). So Isocrates himself apologises for the informality of the work.

It would then appear that Isocrates shows significant differences between his most carefully cultivated works, he is said to have spent ten years in the composition of Work 4, and his informal forensic speeches and the single work which is directly comparable with the forensic speeches. It will be recalled that Isocrates' own son preferred to think that his father had not written any forensic speeches and Isocrates himself appeared to regard them as unworthy of his talents.

That significant differences are found in such circumstances need occasion no surprise. Any stylistic method is vulnerable to the writer who deliberately composes in a convention. If any contemporary were asked to write a formal address on a royal occasion it might read more like Kipling or Shakespeare than his personal prose.

It should be noted that, within the same genre, Works 4, 5 and 12 are entirely consistent and cover forty-one years of Isocrates' career; Works 2 and 18 are twenty-eight years apart, Works 15 and 18 are forty-eight years apart. In other words within the same genre his works are consistent and excluding in turn only the two extremes of genre, the periods of consistency are forty-eight and forty-one years.

There is obviously no difficulty in comparing works of the same genre, or of allied genre; the difficulties arise only in the contrast of extremes in a writer who cultivated a grand manner which he thought suited great occasions.

The usefulness of sentence length distributions can now be summarised. They have been tested not only over the authors tested here and in Wake's paper, but also in Leontius of Byzantium who wrote as late as the sixth century A.D. Samples have been counted in all the prose writers issued by the Oxford Press and by the end of 1965 the samples will cover all the prose writers in the Loeb series.

No exceptions have come to light except when the limits of the hypothesis were being established by deliberately applying it to extreme cases, such as dialogue, all of which lie outside the definition of continuous homogeneous prose.

Even if an exception had been found it would hardly matter for the consistency of sentence length distributions cannot be vitiated by any one exception; it would need a significant proportion of exceptions to render analysis unreliable. If such a proportion exists and no instance of it has come to light so far in the examination of over thirty prose writers, we have been victims of a malign coincidence of the most staggering kind.

Sentence length distributions must be used with respect for their limitations. They do not apply to dialogue, commentary and any other kinds of heterogeneous or discontinuous prose. There is also a minimum sample size.

It would also appear that they must be used with caution when the time covered by the samples is much over fifty years. As has already been seen, the difficulty is simply that Isocrates is the only author whose works extend over a long enough period to let the effect of such periods of time be seen and even then the demonstration is not conclusive. Wake argued for a similar change in sentence length in the works of Plato where there is the complication of dialogue.

An argument based on sentence length must be exclusive. You can never prove that two works were written by one author but only that two works cannot have been written by one author. As can be seen from the works of Demosthenes this one test alone excludes from the population of an author's works the majority of those which have been excluded, on quite different grounds, by scholars of traditional types.

It is important for the reader to grasp that this kind of analysis does not simply rest on the majority opinion of classical scholars. This analysis is part of a wider investigation of how the human brain works in storing and using words. It has been shown by Dr A. E. Roy ("On a Method of Storing Information" *The Bulletin of Mathematical Biophysics*, Vol. 22, 1960), that habits of the type represented by constancy of sentence length distributions are a consequence of learning, remembering and forgetting. Indeed Dr Roy predicted that habits of this type would change with failing memory and the disappearance of the power to absorb new knowledge.

The second point of importance is that any alternative interpretation to a difference of authorship, where a statistically significant difference in sentence length is present, has been excluded. When it has been shown that genre, subject matter and long periods of time do not affect the distributions, what else remains to affect them? This is a subject to which we shall return. Whatever may be said of one test of authorship, the agreement of half a dozen independent tests adds a new dimension to the argument. One would hesitate to build very much on the slender foundation of a single test, unless you were of a speculative or theological turn of mind, but a battery of tests validate each other.

CHAPTER SIX

THE OCCURRENCE OF SOME COMMON WORDS

AN AUTHOR who sits down to write about the sea and ships can be expected to use certain words in writing about them—"sea", "ships", "tides", "winds". He may show a personal preference for some of these words or he may try to enrich his prose by using such synonyms as "vessels", "boats", or "craft". In either case much of his vocabulary depends on his subject matter and it is difficult to transfer any stylistic argument from one subject to another. There are other complications of vocabulary studies which cannot be neglected. Professor J. Bronowski, in *The Common Sense of Science*, points out that Pope uses three or four times as many colour words, and uses them ten times as often, as Shakespeare, but Pope lived when Newton had opened the full range of the spectrum for the first time.

The simplest way to exclude the effect of subject matter is to look either at the patterns of words and not at the words themselves, as is done in sentence length distributions, or at the occurrence of those words which are literally inescapable, the words which must be used in any context and can be regarded as neutral in any single context. As has already been illustrated, these are the connective, the filler words. Though few in number they are repeated often and so make up a surprising proportion of any text.

Table 12 shows the most frequently occurring words in the Greek New Testament. It will be seen that six words make up nearly thirty-one per cent of the whole text. In classical authors the rate of occurrence of these words varies, but generally those are the six most frequently used words in any Greek prose writer.

One of these words, the commonest word of all, the definite article, is too much dependent on subject matter to be the basis of a simple stylistic test. The definite article is used with nouns and adjectives and verbs all of which depend on subject matter. It is possible to approach this problem from another angle and to look at the proportion of nouns which has an accompanying definite article and the proportion which does not have a definite article. This appears to be a stylistic habit of long duration with prose writers and it is now being investigated, but the simple occurrence of the definite article is not suited to a general test.

Now it must be clearly understood that an examination of this kind has nothing to do with the meaning of these common words, the usage of these words, or how they might be translated into any language, or any such grammatical or semantic connotation. They are to be looked at as a habit. How often does this writer use this word? How does he spread it through his book? These are the questions to which we address ourselves.

Some scholars' reaction to this procedure is to cry nonsense, but it is their reaction which has no sense. There is a sound analogy between this analysis and the treatment of human beings. For many purposes, and they are the most important purposes, we talk of men and women as good, kind, wise, mean, foolhardy and so on down the catalogue of value judgments, but when the police, or any other body, wishes to be sure of identity they abandon the description of values, they do not look for a man who has a generous heart but for a man who has recognisable physical features which can be described in numerical terms. They record height and weight and the patterns on the end of your fingers or on the soles of your feet, which experience has shown to be much more reliable than the most detailed literary descriptions.

So we concern ourselves with questions such as:

Is this word "kai", or is it any other word? In the next twenty successive words how many are "kai" and how many are not "kai"?

This is not rejecting the literary scholars' approach and invalidating his information, it is producing a new kind of information. This information may be totally irrelevant to many situations, but for the purposes of identification it is very relevant indeed.

When an investigation of this kind is begun it is possible to have a fair idea, based on the observation of other phenomena, of what to expect. It seems reasonable to suppose that any author will use a word, such as "kai", at about the same rate in any works which he wrote within a short period of time. The real unknowns were whether or not the rate of such usage in any author changed with time and whether or not his rate varied so much that it overlapped the rates of other authors and so rendered their works indistinguishable one from another.

To pick up the basic principle already described, if a word like "kai" occurs about once in twenty words of text, then the probability of its occurrence is $p = 0.05$. In one thousand words of text you would expect to find "kai", 1,000 x 0·05 = 50 times. As was said before, though it cannot be predicted from first principles how often an author will use a word like "kai", the number of times he does use it in a few thousand words of text will give an estimate sufficiently accurate for practical purposes.

If a word has a probability of occurring of $p = 0·05$ then the probability of it not occurring is obviously 0·95. If the occurrence complies with the conditions of simple sampling we can state three regularities about the occurrence of the word.

The first is that if the word occurs, on the average at a rate p, the standard error of the proportion p is $\sqrt{\left(\dfrac{PQ}{N}\right)}$ where N is the total number of words in the sample. And exactly as in the case of sentence length distributions only one sample in twenty, drawn from a single population, will lie outside the limits of two standard errors from the population mean and only about one in three hundred outside the limits of three standard errors.

Thus we can construct a simple table for the proportion of any word in an author's works. The headings would be the number of words in the sample, the number of "kais"—or whatever word we are interested in—the proportion of "kai", the standard error of the proportion. Then we can test the hypothesis, as before, that all of an author's works can be treated as a single population and each work as a sample drawn from that population.

Where it can be shown that samples of these common words do lie within these limits and obey the rules for simple sampling, two other theorems can be used.

Given that the rate of occurrence follows the rules of simple sampling then the number of "kais" to be found in small samples can be predicted, as will shortly be illustrated, by the terms of a mathematical pattern known as a Poisson distribution. An obvious size of small sample to choose is the reciprocal of the rate of occurrence. If "kai" is about one word in twenty then look at samples of twenty words. The number of samples with one, two, three, etc. "kais" can be predicted by the Poisson distribution for which z is 1.

The third way of looking at the occurrence of a common word which can be treated in terms of simple sampling is to look at the spacing of occurrences. The Poisson distribution was a way of looking at the number of occurrences of "kai" in an interval of, say, twenty words. This is the way of looking at the number of intervals of any given size which come between successive occurrences.

Though these are two ways of looking at the same thing, it can be useful to try both as they test rather different aspects of the distribution. An unduly large number of long intervals between "kais" would show up at once in this second treatment because the expected number of large intervals is small and two or three added to this small number makes a large difference. The Poisson test applied to the same data would not have shown any significant results. The creation of the large intervals would, in this analysis, have only added a few more samples to the number which had no "kai". The number of such samples is expected to be large and a few added to this number would go undetected.

To examine intervals a negative exponential is fitted to the data.

The three ways of looking at the occurrence of a common word which conforms to the rules of simple sampling are set out below.

1. For a word which occurs at a rate p so that the proportion in a sample is p, the standard error of the proportion is $\sqrt{\left(\dfrac{PQ}{N}\right)}$.

Where p is the proportion of words which are the word under examination, q is the proportion of other words and N is the number of words in the sample.

2. Where the expectation is z that the word will occur in a sample, then the number of samples with n words occurring in them can be calculated from the successive terms of the expression, the Poisson distribution

$$P = \varepsilon^{-z} \left\{ 1 + z + \frac{z^2}{2!} + \frac{z^3}{3!} \dots \frac{z^n}{n!} \right\}$$

In this expression e is the base of natural logarithms and the symbol $n!$ means that you multiply together all the numbers from one up to n. This product, called factorial n, is $1 \times 2 \times 3$ for $3!$ and so equals six.

3. If we have a sample of N spaces between successive occurrences of the word under examination and m is the reciprocal of the average space, i.e. the number of words between the first and last occurrences divided by the number of spaces between them, the number of intervals which whose length is the difference between the word $w1$ and the word $w2$ will be given by

$$P = N \left\{ e^{-mw1} - e^{-mw2} \right\}$$

All this is easier to appreciate in an example, and before going on it may be helpful to follow the occurrence of one word in a single sample just to see how the habitual usage can be expressed in these mathematical terms.

In the Epistle to the Galatians there are seventy-two "kais" among 2,233 words in the text of Souter. There are therefore 111 complete small samples of twenty successive words. The proportion of "kai" in the work is $\frac{72}{2233} = 0.0322$. Thus the expectation for each twenty word sample is twenty times this, 0.644. This is the probabilility of "kai" occurring in each sample. This being so the number of samples expected to have one "kai", two "kais", three "kais", etc., can be worked out in terms of the Poisson distribution and the comparison between what we expect to find and what we do find when a computer counts the "kais" is the samples as shown in Table 13.

For this table chi squared is 1.2 for two degrees of freedom which means that differences as large as those found between what was expected and what was counted would arise, by chance alone, about three times in every four trials.

The spacing between "kais" can be examined by working out the negative exponential of section three. The probability of the occurrence of spaces extending from the w_1th word to the w_2th word is given by $e^{-mw1} - e^{-mw2}$.

In the Epistle to the Galatians there are seventy-two "kais". The first "kai" is word thirteen and the last "kai" is word 2,198. The seventy-one spaces between the seventy-two "kais" total $2,198 - 13$ words $= 2,185$ words.

Thus the average space is 30.77 words. The reciprocal of 30.77, 1 divided by 30.77, is 0.0325 and this is m for the expression above.

The value of e is 2.7183 and the logarithm of e to the base ten is 0.4343. To find how many spaces you would expect to find having between one and ten words, you multiply the logarithm of e to the base ten, 0.4343, by m, 0.0325, and by ten, for the tenth word. This gives $0.4343 \times 0.0325 \times 10 = 0.1412$ As we are interested in the value of e^{-mt}, in this case, $e^{-0.0325 \times 10}$, we subtract the result from the logarithm of 1 which is 0.0000 This gives 1.8588 and the antilog of this is 0.722. This is the probability in which we are interested and if we multiply this by the number of spaces, seventy-one, we get 51.3. As there are seventy-one spaces and 51.3 will be more than ten words, the number between one word and ten is given by subtracting 51.3 from $71 = 19.7$. In Table 14 are set out the calculated numbers of spaces and beside them are displayed the spaces as counted by computer. For the table chi squared is 4.1 for three degrees of freedom, indicating that differences between what was expected and what was counted would arise by chance about one trial in every six and so can hardly be counted as significant.

When looking at the occurrence of a word in sentences other mathematical resources must be employed, it is obvious that the probability of finding a word in a long sentence is much greater than the probability of finding the same word in a short sentence. As will be seen in later examples, the result of such a variable probability is a distribution called a negative binomial.

THE OCCURRENCE OF "KAI"

All the operations described above are conditional on the occurrence of the word conforming to the conditions of simple sampling. "Kai" was used as an example but it has yet to be shown that the occurrence of "kai" does satisfy the conditions for simple sampling and it is not obvious that the occurrence will conform to the rules of simple sampling.

Words are not isolated events like the tosses of a coin or the throws of a dice. Words have contextual ties and if they can be compared to any simple chance mechanism it might be a pack of cards which have become tacky so that some groups of cards tend to stick together.

The simplest way to show the difference between the occurrence of a word and the occurrence of a purely random event is to look at successive occurrences of the event. "Kai" occurs at a rate of about 0·05, so that two successive occurrences of "kai" would be found, if the occurrence was a matter of pure chance, at a rate of $0·05 \times 0·05 = 0·0025$, i.e. in four hundred words of text you could expect to find two successive "kais". In Greek prose two successive "kais" are found about once in a million words of text.

Not only do these common words depart from random behaviour, there are also some rare words which occur comparatively frequently in pairs. "It is very very cold today"—"Oh that this too too solid flesh."

The point which is being made is a simple one but it is important. Words are not the product of a mechanism but are used by writers in the context of a culture. Statistical terms can be used to describe certain features of style and of language but words are not emitted by a random generator.

One result of this fact is that any stylistic test based on a single word must sometimes be vulnerable to a special relation of the text to the word. For example it seems reasonable to suppose that the occurrence of the Greek verb "to be", "einai", will be independent of subject matter. The verb "to be" expresses a general relationship, X is, or was, or will be Y. The relationship does not depend on the particular X and Y. It is true that the different tenses might be used by a prophet with an apocalyptic bias or an old man looking back but the sum of all tenses is not likely to depend on the subject matter. The second book of the History of Herodotus however begins with a description of the River Nile, not only must this be a catalogue of the geographical information—"the Nile is—and—its tributaries are—" but Herodotus goes on to describe how the River Nile is worshipped as a Divine Being by the Egyptians and it is not possible to discuss "being" without using the verb "to be". So this passage has many more occurrences of "einai" than any other comparable passage in Herodotus. It is passages of this nature which make it essential to develop a number of stylistic tests and to use them together.

To show that the occurrence of a word complies with the conditions of simple sampling, it is necessary to count the rate of occurrence in a number of samples and carry out a chi squared test on the figures. Table 15 shows the occurrence of "kai" in thirty-two samples from the History of Thucydides. Each sample is fifty successive sentences, taken in groups of four, from the start of each book of the History. To carry out the chi squared test, each number of occurrences of "kai", ninety-six in the first sample, is squared, that is multiplied by itself, $96 \times 96 = 9,216$, and this figure is divided by the number of words in the sample, 1,370, to give 6·727. This operation is completed for each sample and yields thirty-two figures. Added together they total 196·12. The total number of occurrences of "kai" is 2,774 and of all the words in all the samples 39,851. The total number of occurrences of "kai" is squared and divided by the total number of words in all the samples. The result is 193·10. The difference in the two totals 196·1 and 193·1 is 3·0. To get the value for chi squared this figure of 0·91 must be divided by the product of the proportion of "kai", 0·0696 and the proportion of words not "kai", 0·9304; the product is 0·0648. Chi squared is 3·0 divided by 0·0648, which is 46·2. To be able to interpret this figure for chi squared it is necessary to know the number of degrees of freedom associated with the figure. In the circumstances of this table the number of degrees of freedom is the number of free choices within the table. If you take a sample of two thousand words and there are one hundred "kais" in the sample, then there must be 1,900 occurrences of words other than "kai". Thus for any given sample, one line in Table 15, there is only one free choice and so one degree of freedom. If the totals for all the samples are fixed, as they are by the selection of the samples, then the last entry in the column must also be fixed, for it is the grand total less the total for all the samples except the last. So the number of free choices in a table like this is one less than the number of rows and one less than the number of columns, $32 - 1 \times 2 - 1 = 31$.

Entering the tables of chi squared in any set of statistical tables for thirty-one degrees of freedom will give the values of p appropriate to the value of chi squared. Actually thirty-one degrees of freedom is a value rarely printed, thirty and thirty-two are usually given. For thirty degrees of freedom chi squared is 43·8 for $p = ·05$. For thirty-two degrees of freedom chi squared is 46·2 for $p = ·05$. So only once in twenty trials would difference as large as these arise by chance. However these differences are not spread through the text but are concentrated where Herodotus has copied from a source. Where he writes in free composition the differences are not significant.

Table 16 shows the corresponding figures for a set of thirty-six samples taken in a similar way from the History of Herodotus. For these samples chi squared is 32·4 for thirty-five degrees of freedom, so that $p = 0·50$. (A simple rule to remember is that for more than a few degrees of freedom, chi squared is equal to the number of degrees of freedom when p is about 0·50.) As before, the differences between samples are only those to be expected in random sampling.

Table 17 shows the occurrence of "kai" in some samples from the dialogues of Plato. For the seven samples, if Epistle seven is omitted, chi squared is 3·0 for six degrees of freedom and for the eight samples, if Epistle seven is included, chi squared is 3·20 for seven degrees of freedom corresponding to $p = 0·80$ and $p = 0·90$ respectively. It is obvious that these dialogues, and the seventh Epistle, show much the same rate of using "kai".

The Axiochus is a work recognised to be spurious and though it has a higher proportion of "kai" than any of the genuine works of Plato the proportion is not significantly higher.

Table 18 shows the occurrence of "kai" in some samples from the works of Clement of Alexandria. For all nine samples chi squared is 13·6 for eight degrees of freedom and so $p = 0·10$.

These illustrations show that for authors who write in the same, or in similar, literary forms, the rate of occurrence of "kai" remains sensibly constant over long periods of time, about thirty years in the case of both Thucydides and Herodotus, and over wide ranges of subject matter.

In an investigation of this kind where the aim is to establish general principles about a whole class of writers, it is the exceptions which are important. The exceptions can be particular or general. First to be looked at are two particular exceptions.

Table 19 shows the occurrence of "kai" in the two Epistles of

Clement. For the table as a whole, all the samples from both Epistles, chi squared is 18·1 for six degrees of freedom, a value found by chance rather less than once in a hundred trials. For the five samples of I Clement chi squared is 10·7 for four degrees of freedom; for this p is just over 0·01. An inspection of the table reveals that Sample 1 has a high rate of occurrence of "kai".

In the Loeb text II Clement occupies seventeen complete pages, so that the average number of "kais" per page is just under ten. Thirteen of the seventeen pages have between seven and eleven occurrences and only one page, has more than fifteen occurrences and this page (p. 156), has nineteen occurrences, six of which are direct quotations from Isaiah 66. Now I Clement sample one has two pages with nineteen occurrences and one with twenty-five occurrences. All three pages have extensive quotations and page 24 of the Loeb text, which has twenty-five occurrences, is a paraphrase of the story of Abraham from Genesis. Thus the high rate of occurrence of "kai" is due to the author departing from free composition and basing his prose on the words of other men.

If sample one is left out, the remaining samples have chi squared 6·6 for five degrees of freedom and for this $p = 0·25$, so differences as large as are found between samples would arise, by chance alone, about once in every four trials.

Table 20 shows the occurrence of "kai" in six samples, chosen as for sentence length, from the History of Diodorus Siculus. For the six samples chi squared is 11·3 for five degrees of freedom and so p is just under 0·05, the level which would be considered significant. An inspection of the text shows that the fourth sample, from Book 21, is the reason for the significant difference. A reading of Book 21 reveals that section 21 of this book has only one "kai" in a run of fourteen sentences. The section is a speech said by Dindorf to derive from the debate of the Tarentines and the conversation of Pyrrhus. This section is not the free composition of Diodorus Siculus. If the sample from Book 21 is excluded from the table, then chi squared is 4·6 for five degrees of freedom. The differences between the samples are only those expected in random sampling.

Before leaving these two examples it may be worth recording that the normal use of quotations by an author do not result in significant stylistic differences. It is only when an appreciable part of his text is taken from, or based upon, another author, that such differences appear.

General differences appear when works in contrasting literary forms are compared. Table 21 shows the occurrence of "kai" in the works of Lysias, for the table as it stands chi squared is over eighty for thirty-four degrees of freedom and it is clear that the occurrence of "kai" in the works is not binomial nor does it meet the conditions of simple sampling. Unfortunately the fragmentary natures of many of the works, and the uncertain chronology, prevent any systematic classification of the works. This means that the simplest procedure is to treat all the works as a group which shows a variable rate of using "kai."

As has been pointed out before, for an event which occurs at a rate p for n trials, the mean number of occurrences of the event will be np and the standard error of the proportion of events occurring is $\sqrt{\left(\dfrac{pq}{n}\right)}$ where $q = 1 - p$. If the rate of occurrence varies from one set of trials to another but remains constant for the set, the situation which corresponds to works written with a rate of occurrence which remains unchanged throughout each work but varies from work to work, then the standard error of the rate of occurrence increases by a term due to the changing rate. The standard error of the proportion becomes:

$$S.\ E. = \sqrt{\left\{\left(\frac{P_0\ Q_0}{N}\right) + \frac{N-1}{N}\left(\frac{PQ}{N}\right)\right\}}$$

P, Q — proportion in sample

P_0, Q_0 — proportion in population.

For the thirty-five works of Lysias in the table, the mean of the thirty-five sample means is $0 \cdot 0407$ and the mean rate of occurrence of "kai" in all the samples lumped together is $0 \cdot 0425$. The difference, $0 \cdot 0018$ is not significant. The variance calculated from the formula $\left(\dfrac{PQ}{N}\right)$ for all the thirty-five works is $7 \cdot 4 \times 10^{-4}$ and the variance calculated from the samples is $7 \cdot 5 \times 10^{-4}$. The agreement of the calculated and measured values suggest that the modified expression fits the data. (See Tables 22 and 23).

This example serves to illustrate the disadvantage in this procedure; the population limits are set by the standard errors of the rate of occurrence and as these increase, it is not possible to make any judgment at all about the smaller samples. All the thirty-five works of Lysias lie within a range of two standard errors of the mean rate of occurrence for all the works when allowance is made for the variable expectation.

Table 24 shows the occurrence of "kai" in the works of Isocrates. Taken as a group the works show heterogeneity. If the works are grouped, following the editor of the Loeb text, into genre, the groups are homogeneous.

Class of Work	Works in Group	Chi squared	Degrees of freedom
Epistles	1– 9	12·5	8
Forensic speeches	16–21	10·5	5
Hortatory	2– 3	3·6	1
Epideictic	9–12	4·2	3
Education essays	13, 15	0·1	1

Exactly as before these works can be treated as having been written with a rate occurrence of "kai" constant within each work but varying from work to work. For the twenty-nine works together the mean rate of occurrence of "kai" is 0·0469, the mean of the sample means is 0·0468. The variance calculated is $5·3 \times 10^{-4}$, and measured from the samples it is $5·7 \times 10^{-4}$.

For the one work not by Isocrates the proportion of "kai" is 0·0240. The standard error of this proportion, including the terms for the variable rate is 0·005. This work has a rate of occurrence five standard errors from the mean of all the genuine works.

Table 25 shows the occurrence of "kai" in all the works of Demosthenes. For the thirty-four works accepted as genuine the mean rate of occurrence is 0·0485, the mean of the thirty-four sample means is 0·0482. The variance of the thirty-four sample means is 0·00011 and the theoretical variance calculated from the lumped samples is 0·00044. The variance ratio not quite significant at the 0·05 level. This is acceptable in the circumstances for the only point in lumping together all the works is to see how far the hypothesis can be applied to the greatest of all Greek stylists' writing over a period of more than twenty years and in the widest range of literary form.

The standard errors for the proportion of "kai" calculated on the basis of a variation in the expectation are shown in column five of Table 25. Only three of the spurious works are excluded from the population, Works 25, 48 and 59.

One genuine work, the masterpiece of Demosthenic oratory, On The Crown, Work 18, also lies outside the limits of three standard errors from the mean.

Work 18 is undoubtedly genuine. The result is due to a remarkable run of twenty-five sentences within the sample, sentences 175 to two hundred of the oration. In these are no less than fifty-eight "kais". The twenty-five sentences before have thirty-two "kais", the succeeding twenty-five sentences have twenty-one. The passage is a powerful one where Demosthenes is cataloguing his adversaries, impugning their patriotism and listing their charges against him. The repeated conjunction is used with great effect to link the elements of his argument in patterns of ridicule.

The one other oration of the same type is Work 19, *De Falsa*, and for the two works together chi squared is 1·5 for one degree of freedom.

This example illustrates two difficulties which arise when a body of accepted works belongs to one genre and the questioned work is a rare example of a contrasting genre. When allowance is made for the variation in the rate of occurrence, a decision is only possible where fairly large samples are available. With the usual samples of less than two hundred sentences, it is unlikely that anything but the grossest differences in the rate of occurrence could be distinguished.

The other problem which arises is that the accepting of the natural population of the author's surviving works may mean the population is heavily biased by the preponderance of certain genre and so tend to exclude other literary forms for no other reasons than their rarity among his works.

Demosthenes has two groups of works which have been distinguished by the editor of the text. His political speeches are Works 1 to 9 with 14 to 16; for these chi squared is 12·4 for ten degrees of freedom. His public law speeches are those employed in his suit against his guardians, Works 27 to 31, and for these works chi squared is 6·1 for four degrees of freedom. The two formal orations have been mentioned above. The remainder of the works are private speeches written to suit the particular circumstances of a client. They are in a variety of forms and many of them are thought to have been altered by the client.

The works of the three orators, Lysias, Isocrates and Demosthenes have been used to illustrate that while the comparison of works in the same literary form is straightforward the comparison of works in differing literary forms can be complicated. There is an alternative method of making comparisons which surmounts many of the difficulties of making allowance for a variable rate of occurrence of "kai", and this is to look at the distribution of the word in sentences.

The most searching test of any stylistic method supposed to cover all writers of Greek prose is to apply it to the works of the orators. These men wrote speeches for others to use and consciously adapted their own style to the situation of their clients or the occasion on which the speech was to be used. It is for this reason that three orators are used as illustrations of this method.

Table 22 shows the occurrence of "kai" in the sentences of all those works of Lysias which have more than eighty sentences in them. If Work 2 is excluded, the work widely questioned and rejected by the test of sentence length, then the fit of the occurrence of "kai" in the sentences of all the other works to a negative binomial with the same mean and variance is shown in Table 23. The fit is satisfactory, chi squared is 5·7 for three degrees of freedom. (Two degrees of freedom have been eliminated by using the mean and the variance as a basis of the calculation.) The fit of all the individual works to the expectation derived from the negative binomial is also satisfactory. All the works belong to one population, a conclusion which is hardly surprising as it agrees with the conclusion of the variable expectation method.

Table 24 shows the occurrence of "kai" in the sentences of the works of Isocrates. Excluding Work 1, the work not by Isocrates, and Work 12, the work which shows signs of senility, and Works 15, 20, and 21 and the Epistles all of which have less than sixty sentences, the distribution for all the works is a good fit to a negative binomial with a mean of 1·217 and a variance of 2·345, chi squared being 8·3 for six degrees of freedom. For all the works chi squared is 86·1 for seventy-one degrees of freedom when fitted to the expectation derived from the negative binomial. The value of chi squared for Work 1 is highly significant and as is the value for Work 12. The complication of this method is that these differences might be due to a difference in sentence length distribution and this cannot be decided from an inspection of the distribution in sentences alone. Reference to the rates of occurrence of "kai" in the works, Table 25 shows that the rate in Work 1 is significantly different from the mean rate in all the works but that the occurrence in Work 12 is not significantly different from the mean rate. It will be recalled that Work 12 had a significant difference in sentence length distribution, and this is the cause of the difference of occurrence in the sentences.

It will be seen that this method is not nearly as sensitive to changes in literary form as the alternative method. Work 12 is the only exception; all the other works, in their variety of forms, come from a single population.

The other disadvantage of this method is that it relies on sentence marking and as the original texts had little punctuation, some scholars are reluctant to accept any judgment based on modern punctuation as this has been added by modern editors. It has been shown a number of times in a variety of circumstances that editorial differences are negligible compared to sampling differences but there are circumstances where it might be diplomatic to avoid the use of sentence markings. It is for that reason that the occurrence of "kai" in small samples of twenty successive words is shown in Table 25 for all the works of Demosthenes. For all the works large enough to provide ninety samples or more, (twenty-four of these are accepted by Rose as genuine), the distribution is a good fit to a Poisson distribution with the same constants. The individual works also fit Poisson distributions but there are significant differences between means of works in different genre. Exactly as before there are three groups, the political works, the two elaborate speeches, 18 and 19, and Works 27 to 31. This treatment shows no advantage over the simple proportion of "kai" in the work.

It would appear that the rate of using "kai" for works of the same literary form is consistent over long periods of time and wide ranges of subject matter. Thus comparison of works in the same, or similar, form is a simple and straightforward matter. When comparison must be made between works of differing literary forms the alternatives are to look at the distribution in sentences or to make allowance for a variation in the rate of occurrence between works. The first method is not affected by anything less than the widest extremes of genre, indeed the changes of senility afford the only exception, but it is necessary to make sure that any statistically significant difference found is due to the change in the occurrence of "kai", and not to some anomalous sentence length distribution. The methods based on allowing for the variable rate of occurrence can be used but it is vulnerable to two factors. It needs larger samples, a stringent limitation as the three orators whose works have been used as illustrations of this section 117 surviving works, but fifty-two of these have less than one hundred sentences and only twenty-seven have more than two hundred sentences. Thus a method which needed samples of over two hundred sentences would apply to not much over one-fifth of the works, a method which could be used profitably with one hundred sentence samples would apply to more than half. The other situation in which this method is inapplicable is where there is a group of works in one genre, or in a related genre and a small number of works in a very contrasting genre. This, as was seen in Demosthenes, can bias the population so that works might be excluded from the population only because they are scarce and extreme examples of his range of literary forms.

The comparison of the occurrence of "kai" in sentences for works in the same literary form is straightforward. Table 27 shows the occurrence of "kai" in samples of two hundred sentences from the History of Herodotus. The distribution is not Poisson; the variance is appreciably greater than the mean, it can be fitted to a negative binomial distribution. When an individual author is under examination it is generally possible to fit the data to some distribution. Log normal and truncated normal distributions are often suitable, but there is no one distribution which will fit all authors. The simplest procedure is to look at the occurrences in a contingency table. A contingency table merely sets out a series of observations, such as those in Table 28, and uses the probabilities estimated from the table as a guide to the probabilities of the population. In Table 28 there are 1,600 sentences in eight samples. 337 sentences have no "kai" so that an estimate of p for the occurrence of a sentence with no "kai" is $\frac{337}{1600} = 0\cdot211$ and the number expected in a sample of two hundred sentences is $200 \times 0\cdot211 = 42\cdot2$. Of course you cannot get 42·2 sentences with no "kai"; you can only get whole numbers, and so to calculate chi squared you have to make an allowance for this fact by reducing all the figures which are above expectation by 0·5 and increasing all those which are below expectation by 0·5.

For the whole table chi squared is 53·3 for forty-two degrees of freedom, p is about 0·15 so that differences as large as those found between these samples would come about by chance alone, about one trial in every six.

There is a possibility that some of these samples might represent high values from a group which had a low average while other samples were low values from a group with high averages. This possibility can be excluded by an analysis of variance, shown at the foot of Table 28. This operation is fully discussed in any textbook of statistics, and is a means of dividing up the variations in the table between those variations which are due to differences between the samples and those which occur within the samples. The result is to show that the possibility can be dismissed in this case; the differences between the samples compared to those found within the samples can be explained as due to chance alone.

A further refinement would be to use maximum likelihood estimators, but this method gives results very similar to those obtained by the contingency table and the difference between the methods is so small that no case would ever be decided upon such a narrow margin.

Table 28 shows the similar data for the samples from Thucydides. Readers who want to see comparable tables for Aristotle, Plato, Plutarch, Xenophon and Strabo should consult "The Authorship of the

F

Pauline Corpus" (A. Q. Morton in *The New Testament in Historical and Contemporary Perspective*, ed. Barclay, Blackwell, Oxford, 1965).

The examination of the use of "kai" can be summarised thus, when comparing works in the same literary form the rate of occurrence of "kai" can be looked at either in a two by two contingency table such as Tables 27 and 28 or by calculation of the standard errors for simple sampling. When a comparison between works in contrasting literary forms must be made, allowance must be included for the variable rate of occurrence or the distribution in sentences examined. There are circumstances in which one method might be more useful than the other. In fact it would be a routine matter to examine the occurrence of "kai" in small samples, in terms of the spacing between occurrences and the occurrence in sentences by a single computer programme. For any case of disputed authorship to be dealt with in detail all these patterns would be looked at.

THE OCCURRENCE OF THE PARTICLE "DE"

Most writers of Greek prose use the particle "de" not quite as often as they use the conjunction "kai"; it is the exceptional author who has more occurrences of "de" than of "kai" in his text. The particle is used at the beginning of a sentence but never stands as the first word in the sentence, usually as the second or third word. "De" is rarely found as the fourth word in the sentences; some authors will never have it in this position but others will have it as the fourth word about one sentence in six or eight hundred. Later in sentences "de" occurs in a number of clausal constructions.

The purely positional distinction which is made in the usage of "de" at the beginning of a sentence makes it possible to ask a simple question: Does this sentence begin with "de" or does it not?—the question to be interpreted as meaning does the sentence have "de" as its second or third word or does it not. A choice of this kind is likely to produce a binomial distribution and its treatment can be correspondingly simple.

Table 29 shows the occurrence of "de" at the beginning of the sentences of each book of the Histories of Herodotus and of Thucydides. In each case the samples differs only by the expected differences of random sampling. The samples from Herodotus have chi squared 13·4 for eight degrees of freedom and for Thucydides it is 5·5 for seven degrees of freedom.

Table 30 shows the occurrence of "de" at the start of the sentences of those works of Lysias which are long enough to provide a reliable sample. For all nine works chi squared is 7·0 for eight degrees of freedom and the questioned Work 2 has just about the average rate of occurrence.

Table 31 shows the occurrence of "de" at the start of all the sentences in the Demosthenic Corpus. For the twenty-seven accepted works which have ninety sentences or more chi squared is 10·9 for twenty-six degrees of freedom, so that ninety-nine times in every hundred trials sampling differences would be larger than those found between the samples.

For the genuine works the mean rate of occurrence of "de" at the beginning of sentences is 0·225 and the proportion of sentences which do not start with "de" is 0·775. Calculating the standard errors of the proportion in terms of simple sampling and taking two standard errors as the population limits, there is excluded from the population of Works 14 of those rejected by Rose out of the twenty which he rejects and are large enough to provide samples. Of the accepted works, one, Work 6, would be excluded. An examination of the work shows why this is so. In this work there is a run of sentences which summarise his opponent's case and especially from sentence twenty-five to sentence sixty, these begin with a few words taken from the opponent's argument and put, by the editor of the Oxford Text, in quotation marks.

Table 32 shows the occurrence of "de" at the start of the sentences in two works of Clement of Alexandria. There is no significant difference between the two works in respect of this habit.

Table 34 shows the occurrence of "de" at the beginning of the sentences of the works of Isocrates. There is a significant difference between the works. Of the two possible explanations of this difference, the passage of time or the change in literary form, the first can be excluded. The rank correlation co-efficient for the nineteen works large enough to provide useful samples is 0·39 and for this value $t = 1·7$ when it would reach the 0·05 level of significance at 4·3.

The alternative explanation, that the difference is due to the contrast in literary form is acceptable for the grouping if all the works, following the Loeb editor, shows homogeneity within the group.

Group	Works	Chi squared	Degrees of Freedom
Forensic speeches	16–19	4·2	3
Hortatory	2– 3	3·0	1
Epideictic	9–12	5·6	3
Educational	13, 15	0·5	1
Miscellaneous political speeches	4–8, 14	10·0	5

The only group with which the rejected work one could be included is the hortatory pair, Works 2 and 3.

Table 34 shows the occurrence of "de" in five works of Plutarch. The first two are consistent, chi squared is 0·1 for one degree of freedom and the next pair, the two lives, are also consistent, chi squared is 0·8 for one degree of freedom. If the fifth work, the Lives of the Ten Orators, is included with the two lives, chi squared rises to 14·8 for two degrees of freedom and for this value p is less than 0·001.

Thus it appears that Plutarch has two habits, one for his pure prose and another for his dialogues and diatribes. Even with the complication of two different rates, the spurious work, The Lives of the Ten Orators, is excluded from the Corpus.

Table 35 shows the occurrence of "de" at the beginning of the sentences of some works of Josephus. Josephus is an interesting writer to examine because he wrote some of his works himself and then employed assistants to write other works in a better Greek style, aware that his own Greek was considered rough and Semitic.

The Antiquities is the work which Josephus wrote himself. For all the samples in the table chi squared is 18·2 for nine degrees of freedom, p just under 0·05, and so the differences between the samples would be considered significant. For the four samples from the Antiquities chi squared is 1·9 for three degrees of freedom, the differences between samples are not significant, and for the four samples from the Jewish War chi squared is 6·6 for three degrees of freedom, again the differences are not significant. For the two samples from The Life, chi squared is 2·6 for one degree of freedom, the difference not significant. The difference in the proportion of sentences which start with "de" in the Antiquities and in the Jewish War is significant but it needs samples of four hundred sentences to show clearly that it is so. If the samples are amalgamated into four hundred sentences the number of occurrences is 200 and 199 for the Antiquities, 187 and 170 for the Jewish War and 178 for the Life. It is clear that the Life and the Jewish War are consistent.

It would then appear that Josephus' use of a literary secretary, or ghost writer, changed his stylistic habit but the change was slight.

The use of "de" as the second or third word in a sentence would appear to be a stylistic habit of some permanence. It is a simple habit and so cannot be a very efficient discriminator. If an author writes half of his sentences using a "de" at the beginning of them p and q are both 0·5 and so $p.q$ is 0·25 and the square root of $p.q$ is 0·5. This means that a sample of one hundred sentences will give a standard error of five per cent and this sample could only be distinguished from other samples of the same size which differed in the rate of use by twenty per cent. Samples of two hundred sentences would reduce this margin to thirteen per cent. Against this limitation can be set the fact that authors do differ widely in their habitual use of "de" in this position. The test is independent of sentence length and is affected only by marked differences in literary form.

THE LATER OCCURRENCES OF "DE"

The particle "de" also occurs in sentences in later positions where it is used, sometimes coupled with another particle, in a number of constructions. The clauses which involve the use of "de" can be classified in a number of ways and it is clear that there are some types of sentence which are likely to have "de" in them and other types of sentence are most unlikely to have the word.

The word "but" or any other qualification has no place in a declaration of love or war.

The simplest procedure is therefore to regard the presence or absence of "de" as an attribute of a sentence. Support for the view that the occurrence of the particle "de" is connected to the occurrence of certain types of sentence can be had from an examination of the simple occurrence in samples. If the samples are large, over two hundred sentences, the proportion of "de" in the sample confirms the rules of simple sampling and the difference between samples are only those expected to occur when samples are drawn from one population. But if the samples are reduced then the differences between samples begin to exceed the random differences expected to occur. Inspection of the samples shows why this is so; the word "de" is rare in any author, occurring only about ten or twenty times in any sample of one hundred sentences so that about ninety of the sentences in the sample will have no occurrence of "de" in them. Six or eight sentences will have a single occurrence and the sample may or may not have one sentence with four or even five occurrences. It is the presence or absence of the comparatively rare sentences with more than two occurrences which create the significant differences between small samples. If the sentences are examined in a contingency table these exceptional sentences go into the cell "two or more", or even for some authors, "one or more", and so the effect of the high proportion of "de" in the sentence is reduced and the differences between samples are only the expected differences of random sampling.

Table 36 shows the occurrence of "de" in the later positions in the sentences of the History of Herodotus. For the table as a whole chi squared is 23·5 for sixteen degrees of freedom, for sample four chi squared is 7·7 so that $p = 0.02$, a difference which is hardly significant in the context.

Table 37 shows the occurrence of "de" in the later positions of the sentences of the History of Thucydides. For the table chi squared is 14·3 for fourteen degrees of freedom.

Table 38 shows the occurrence of "de" in the later positions in all the works of Isocrates. The table as a whole exhibits heterogeneity but if the works are separated into the different literary form, then there is homogeneity within the form. For Works 16 to 21 chi squared is 12·6 for six degrees of freedom; for Works 2 and 3 it is 2·8 for two degrees; for nine to twelve 2·3 for six degrees; for Works 13 to 15 0·1 for two degrees; for Works 4 to 8 with Work 14, 10·0 for fifteen degrees of freedom. Work 1, the rejected work, would not belong to any of these groups.

An alternative treatment of the particle "de" is to deal with all occurrences together and then the occurrences of the word at the start of sentences, so that the later occurrences are lumped with the other occurrences. There are circumstances where one method may be preferred to the other, the only point to watch is that the total information, all the occurrences of "de", can be divided in two ways with only one degree of freedom. In other words if you take all the occurrences, then you can examine those which start sentences or those which do not, but you cannot assume that the total, the proportion which start sentences and the number which do not are three independent pieces of information; they are not, for one piece is simply the sum of the two others.

THREE COMMON WORDS

The next most frequent words in Greek prose are the preposition "en" meaning "in"; the verb "to be", "einai"; and the adjective which has become the personal pronoun equivalent to "he", "she", "it" and "they". These words occur at rates of around 0·01, and so a hundred sentences can be expected to have only fifteen to twenty occurrences. The distribution of these words in twenty-word samples is often found to be identical with the distribution in sentences because the number of sentences with more than two or three occurrences is so small that it must be included with the double or treble occurrence.

The most important point to grasp about these words is that they are not always independent of subject matter. If you write about circles and circumferences, the word "in" is likely to be frequently used; if you write a description of a place, you must often say "it is" or "there are"; if you write in the first person you may say "I" but if you write in the third person "he" will predominate. The result of this connection between the word and certain contexts is that works must be compared which are similar in the relation of word and subject matter. The exceptions are not many but they are important.

Table 39 shows the occurrence of "en" in the History of Herodotus and Table 40 shows the comparable data also of the first two hundred sentences of each book for the History of Thucydides.

Table 41 shows the occurrence of "en" in the sentences of the works of Isocrates and for the table chi squared is 24·2 for twenty-five degrees of freedom, rejected work, Work 1, has chi squared 4·3 for two degrees of freedom, so in this usage is indistinguishable from the rest of the Corpus.

Table 42 shows the occurrence of "en" in twenty-word samples of all the works of Demosthenes. For the table chi squared is 7·8 for twenty-six degrees of freedom for the twenty-seven accepted works long enough to provide samples. Excluded from this population are six of the rejected works, Works 7, 34, 35, 42, 47 and 49.

THE OCCURRENCE OF "AUTOS"

Table 43 shows the occurrence of "autos" in the samples from the History of Herodotus, and Table 44 comparable samples from the History of Thucydides. Both sets of samples are homogeneous. Table 45 shows samples from Isocrates.

Table 46 shows the occurrence of "autos" in twenty-word samples from the works of Demosthenes. For the twenty-four accepted works chi squared is 67·2 and p is less than 0·001. But three works, 27, 30 and 45, contribute 42·6 to chi squared. These works are consistent with each other and they are all works which involved the relation of one person, Demosthenes or Phormio, to a group of people, Demosthenes' guardians in the case of Works 27 and 30. If the works are then split into two groups, we have twenty works for which chi squared is 24·6 for nineteen degrees of freedom and another group, the works dealing with the suit against the guardians and Work 45, for which chi squared is 6·3 for three degrees of freedom. Excluded from both these groups are nine of the twenty-two rejected works.

This example may serve as a reminder that every statistically significant difference must be examined to make sure that it is not to be explained by any feature of the work before it is decided that the stylistic difference must be accounted for by a difference of authorship.

THE OCCURRENCE OF "EINAI"

Table 47 shows the occurrence of "einai" in the samples from the History of Herodotus. For the eight samples, if Sample 2 is excluded, chi squared is 6·4 for fourteen degrees of freedom. For Sample 2, using for the expectation the other eight samples, chi squared is 40·8 for two degrees of freedom. This is a highly significant difference. An inspection of the text show why it is. Herodotus begins Book 2 with a description of the River Nile and for a few hundred words he describes the Nile, its resources and explains that it is worshipped as a divinity, as a "being", by the Egyptians. It is not possible to discuss "being" without repeating the verb "to be". In no case should a significant difference be interpreted without an examination of the whole text which it covers.

Table 48 shows the occurrence of "einai" in the corresponding samples from the History of Thucydides, and Table 49 shows samples from Isocrates.

Table 51 shows the occurrence of "einai" in small samples in the works of Demosthenes. The accepted works show heterogeneity, but if the works are grouped according to literary form there is homogeneity within the groups. For all the accepted political and public speeches, up to Work 24, chi squared is 34·2 for twenty-eight degrees of freedom and for the orations in the suit the guardians, Works 27, 29 and 30, chi squared is 2·2 for four degrees of freedom. Works 18 and 19 are the elaborate orations, they show no significant difference in the occurrence of "einai" from the simpler public orations.

SUMMARY

Everyone of us has habits, indeed it is a truism to say that we live by habit. We have habits of walking, of speaking, of breathing, of writing; habits of all types. We are sometimes aware of these habits and can alter them by conscious effort but for the most part we exercise control of our habits well below the conscious level and if we are sometimes aware of one habit, we are never called upon to think of six simultaneously.

We have been looking at the habits of Greek prose writers. An author can have purely personal habits, temporary or permanent. His temporary habits can be used to date his works if there is a sufficient number of works and if some of them are known to have been written at particular times. But these personal habits of an author need not be shared by any other writer. Our examination has been of those habits which all writers must share, for everyone who writes must write in sentences and use the common words.

The words may be used in different senses. For example one R.A.F. officer in the last war always asked for cream and voiced the opinion that cream would go with anything. To test this hypothesis we served him sardines with cream for breakfast one day. He ate them. But this experience suggests, to most people at any rate, that "ham and eggs" means a natural coupling but "sardines and cream" is a way of saying "surely not sardines with cream". The word "and" has exactly opposite meanings in the two instances. Yet the phrase could be composed as "ham with eggs"—"sardines with cream". The use of the word involves a number of elements of choice; meaning is one of them but the selection of this word from a number of alternatives which would carry the same meaning is another.

It is possible to classify the usages of "kai", an obvious resource is to look at what it connects, phrases, nouns, adjectives and so on. It may well be that some authors have a habitual preference for one usage over the others but this in no way affects the argument that "kai" has been used. The position is like the biologist who counts people with red hair. There may be many origins of red hair and for some purposes it may be essential to be able to classify the hereditary factors involved, but some useful conclusions can still be drawn from the information which merely deals with the proportion of people who have red hair.

Failure to realise that occurrence of a word is distinguishable from its semantic background can lead to confusion. One critic has announced that sentence length distributions are not to be relied upon because it has been said that there are more than two hundred possible definitions of an English sentence. The task in work of this kind is not to define a sentence but to recognise one. The statistical definition is clear and any criticism of it would have to show that the results depended on the definition used or that the editors of the texts employed had been eccentric. The reader may satisfy himself that no conclusion reached in this work depends upon the definition of a sentence or on the use of one text of the writer.

The examination of the habits of Greek prose writers can be summed up in this way:

1. Greek prose writers have habits which persist over long periods of time and wide ranges of subject matter. Comparisons within the same literary genre can be made with confidence and precision.
2. The habits of writers are affected by change of genre and the

comparison of works of widely differing genre should be made with care and reservations.

3. In all work of this kind the text should be examined to see that the habit is representative of the whole work and not affected by some sections of the work which may be quite unlike the work as a whole.

Of the tests described here two are little affected even by wide ranges of literary form. Sentence length covers all the works of Demosthenes and only fails to take in the extremes of Isocrates' range of genre. The use of "de" at the start of sentences is closely parallel, only the extremes of Isocrates or such a clear division of genre as is found in Plutarch need separate treatment.

These two tests can therefore be used to determine authorship and to eliminate the influence of genre on other tests. The testing of "kai" alone may detect differences which are due to a difference of genre or a difference in authorship. Sentence length and the occurrence of "de" at the start of sentences will decide which interpretation is to be placed upon the evidence.

The other tests based upon the later occurrence of "de" and of "en", "autos" and "einai" are to be regarded as confirmatory. With the small samples available in the New Testament one could only hope to detect gross stylistic differences by an examination of these words and they are the more affected by special relations to the text. As a general rule one may say that the commoner the occurrence the more stable and reliable the test becomes.

To conclude this section it is only necessary to say that the reader should understand that this is not the final account of a piece of scholarship which stands complete. New tests are being devised at the present time. Some of these are developments of the work described here, using other habits or more refined statistical techniques. Other tests will be based on the personal habits of the writers which are likely to be more sensitive indicators of authorship once the way has been opened up for their use by the general indicators, the habits shared by all authors.

In other words we are not claiming that this is a final solution to the problem of the authorship of the Pauline Epistles—it may take ten years to accomplish that. But it would be surprising if the final conclusion differed in anything but detail from what we know now and the assumption that Paul is the author of all fourteen or of the majority of the fourteen Epistles in the Corpus is dead. The further firing will be to perfect the weapons, not to kill the corpse.

CHAPTER SEVEN

THE PAULINE EPISTLES

IN SOME respects the authorship of the Pauline Epistles is a simple problem compared to the authorship of other Greek prose writings. The period of time over which the Epistles can have been written is barely fifteen years. McNeile—in his *Introduction to the New Testament*—gives the two limiting dates as A.D. 51 for Thessalonians and A.D. 62 for Philippians. However opinions may vary on the dating of single letters the period is negligible compared to the forty years over which sentence length distributions have been shown to be consistent.

There is no complication about literary form. The one reservation which might have been expressed, the comparison of a simple personal note like Philemon with the more formal Epistles, does not arise because of the size of Philemon. This brief Epistle, 335 Greek words, will not afford any reliable samples though improving techniques have enabled an opinion on its authorship to be expressed.

The Epistle is not one literary form but many. However, all the Epistles in the Pauline Corpus are of much the same kind; they are letters to groups of people and they have the same range of ecclesiastical subject matter. No one will deny that there are differences between one Epistle and another but it has never been suggested that the Epistles differ from each other in the same way as do the literary genres of Demosthenes or Isocrates. It must be borne in mind that we are not here concerned with the precise classification of literary form but merely with the question as to whether or not there exists in the Pauline Corpus the difference in literary form which was found, in the writings of Isocrates, to create significant statistical differences. In this connection it is interesting to note the observations of some of the authorities. Professor A. M. Hunter describes Romans as a massive theological treatise, but this does not prevent it from being entirely consistent with Galatians.

The real difficulty in the Pauline Epistles is that many of the samples are so short that one could only hope to detect gross stylistic differences. Fortunately such differences do exist and can be clearly seen. It calls for comment that such large differences of style do exist and have not been perceived by scholars who yet claim to pick out single phrases and state categorically that they are not Pauline and have been added by another hand. One can only hope that those who have been favoured by this remarkable close vision will give us a systematic account of the principles on which they make their judgments and demonstrate them on other authors.

NOTES ON SAMPLES

Many of the Pauline Epistles are so short that they afford only one sample. Only Romans, I and II Corinthinans, Galatians and Hebrews are large enough to be divided and Galatians, while providing one large sample, is too short to make division profitable. So only Romans, I and II Corinthians and Hebrews are divided into samples. Of these Epistles Galatians has always been accepted as homogeneous and I Corinthians has only been subject to fitful criticism and is best treated as homogeneous until reason appears for suspecting the hypothesis.

Romans has not only a questioned ending, with its benediction appearing not only at the end of chapter 16 but also at the end of chapters 14 and 15; many scholars have argued for insertions in chapters 1, 2 and 3. This Epistle has therefore been divided into three samples of 150 consecutive sentences and a remainder of 131 sentences, making four samples in all. The middle two samples avoid the questioned material.

II Corinthians has been divided at the end of chapter 9 for reasons too obvious to call for comment. But the first nine chapters of the Epistle have been regarded by a number of scholars as an assembly of fragments and so the first part is divided into a sample of the first hundred sentences and a remainder. Other divisions are not only possible but desirable and this Epistle is treated in two other ways in the technical paper by Levison, Morton and Wake and in the paper on "The Integrity of the Pauline Epistles" (*Journal of the Manchester Statistical Society*, A. Q. Morton, March, 1965).

Three of the Epistles, II Thessalonians, Titus and Philemon are excluded from the analysis as they are not large enough to provide reliable samples in tests of this type.

However it appears that certain characteristics of an author can appear in a short group of sentences and a full post mortem examination of all the Epistles, with a demonstration of the Pauline nature of Philemon, can be read in the paper just mentioned above.

Table 51 sets out the sentence length distributions of all the Pauline Epistles and the constants of the distributions large enough to afford samples.

If Galatians is compared with I Corinthians, no significant difference in the constants is found. If the comparison is extended to include Romans, then there is found to be a significant difference, more than the two standard errors appropriate to two parts of a single work, between the first and third samples in the means and in the third quartiles. The third sample of Romans is compatible with Galatians and I Corinthians but Sample I is not. It would then appear that Romans is heterogeneous and that the site of the anomaly is in the first 150 sentences. Similarly the first sample of II Corinthians is significantly different from the Galatians—I Corinthians samples. This would suggest that II Corinthians is heterogeneous and the site of the anomaly lies in the first sample.

Hebrews is also heterogeneous. Two obvious factors to be looked at are the ending (the last chapter may not be part of the Epistle and so should be excluded from Sample 2) and the extensive Old Testament quotations in the body of the Epistle. If these quotations are excluded the Epistle is further removed from the four major Epistles.

The examination of the constants of these distributions reveals the existence of a group, Group I, of four Epistles, Romans, I and II Corinthians and Galatians, with anomalies in the first samples of both Romans and II Corinthians. Clearly separated from Group I, are the isolated Epistles to the Hebrews and to the Ephesians. Another group, Group 2, is made up of Philippians, Colossians, I and II Thessalonians. The Pastorals cannot be separated from this Group 2 and to it may belong part of the first sample of II Corinthians.

This is entirely a repetition of the findings of Dr W. C. Wake as summarised in the *Hibbert Journal* for October, 1948. The text used differs but the conclusions are unchanged.

THE OCCURRENCE OF "KAI" IN THE EPISTLES

Table 52 shows the occurrence of "kai" in the Epistles. From the proportion of "kai" shown in the first section, A, it is clear that the four major Epistles, from Romans to Galatians, form a group; for the four Epistles chi squared is 6·0 for three degrees of freedom. To this group Philemon could belong. Hebrews is again isolated.

The second section, B, the occurrence in sentences, makes clear that the difference in the occurrence of "kai" is not to be explained as the result of a difference in literary form. If a difference of genre were responsible for the change in proportion, the occurrence of "kai" in sentences would be similar, as illustrated earlier, and significant differences would not be found.

The four major Epistles taken as single samples show no significant difference but when they are examined in sections then a significant difference between the first sample of Romans and the remainder of the Epistle does appear. The distribution reveals that the anomaly is connected with the occurrence of a comparatively large number of sentences with two "kais" in them. There are two passages which show this feature 2·2–2·11 and 5·19–25.

The second feature of the distribution of "kai" in sentences is that there is a significant difference between Ephesians, Philippians and Colossians on the one hand and I and II Timothy on the other. I Thessalonians could belong to either group.

The third section, C, of Table 52 is purely illustrative. The occurrence of "kai" in successive blocks of twenty words can be fitted to a Poisson distribution. In the Pauline Epistles this presentation adds nothing to the information in sections A and B but there might be circumstances where this analysis would be of value.

THE OCCURRENCE OF "DE" IN THE PAULINE EPISTLES

Table 53 shows the occurrence of "de" as the second or third word in the sentences of the Epistles.

Romans is homogeneous, for the four samples chi squared is 4·7 for three degrees of freedom and so $p = 0·2$. I Corinthians is homogeneous, chi squared is 6·2 for three degrees of freedom and so $p = 0·1$. II Corinthians is borderline for chi squared is 4·9 for two degrees of freedom and p lies between 0·1 and 0·05. For the three Epistles chi squared would be 15·8 for eight degrees of freedom and p less than 0·05.

I Corinthians and Galatians are consistent. Romans and II Corinthians, taken as single samples, are significantly different from them but the examination of the parts of the two Epistles shows that the differences arise in the third sample of Romans and the third sample of II Corinthians. Both these lie more than two standard errors of the proportion from the mean of I Corinthians with Galatians, which is 0·237.

The difference in Romans lies between chapter 9, verse 16, and chapter 13, verse 5, and the root of the anomaly can be seen if the text is read in the British and Foreign Bible Society text of 1958. In this text all quotations from the Old Testament are printed bold face and the sample contains a large number of such quotations and enough of them lie at the start of sentences to account for the anomaly. If these are deleted from the sample it is consistent with the others.

The last sample of II Corinthians offers no such obvious explanation but one must have reservations about examining any habit with a periodic element in a composite text.

Once again the first four Epistles form a group, with the reservations noted above, and the Epistle to the Hebrews lies well outside this group. The other point of note is the occurrence in Colossians. This Epistle has a rate distinguishable from the rate in Philippians and as Ephesians has already been shown to be an isolated Epistle it appears that the three Epistles, Ephesians, Philippians and Colossians, are all unique.

Part B of the table shows the occurrences of "de" later in the sentences of the Epistles. These occurrences are so rare that nothing can be usefully derived from the data.

THE OCCURRENCE OF "EN", "AUTOS" AND "EINAI"

The occurrence of the words "en", "autos" and "einai" is shown in Table 54. These words are of very limited value in the Epistles as the samples are too small for consistency to be established. Even if the method least sensitive to variation, the occurrence in sentences, is examined there are likely to be significant differences due to the relation of these words to the text.

They are therefore included only to illustrate the point that, if the preceding work has been correct and the four major Epistles from Romans to Galatians are a group, then this group should be different from the rest of the Epistles, even if, in this case, there can also be expected differences within the group.

I Corinthians and Galatians are consistent, Romans and II Corinthians are significantly different but significant differences are also found between I Corinthians and Galatians on the one hand and all the other Epistles except Hebrews.

This evidence is included for illustrative purposes and no weight is attached to it in argument. It is simply not safe to use it with such small samples.

CONCLUSION

In all tests Romans, I and II Corinthians and Galatians form a group. Within the group, differences are found in parts of Romans and II Corinthians but these Epistles have been shown, by literary analysis, to have anomalies where the statistical evidence indicates them to be.

In other words when the Epistles are taken as a whole they are consistent, when they are examined in detail anomalies emerge but the anomalies correspond to sections of the text already delimited by scholars for quite other reasons than those given here. These anomalies can be explained without questioning the authorship of the whole Epistle.

Between the group and the other Epistles exist a large number of significant differences, some of these larger than any differences known to exist in the writings of any other author of Greek prose regardless of literary form or any other factor. It is not possible to explain these differences without assuming a difference of authorship.

Once it is accepted that the first four major Epistles are by a single author the question arises of deciding who he was. In all this book it is assumed, by definition, that Paul is the man who wrote Galatians and so Paul is the writer of all of Galatians and I Corinthians and of most of Romans and II Corinthians. He may well have written Philemon. There is no evidence which would deny him the authorship of this Epistle.

As soon as you turn to the other Epistles the argument descends to a lower level of certainty. The precision of argument in the first four Epistles derives from our having the four Epistles to examine and having three of them large enough to divide into samples and test for homogeneity. It appears that the remainder of the Epistles come from several hands. Hebrews is unique, as are Ephesians, Philippians and Colossians. I and II Thessalonians make a pair, as do I and II Timothy. But in each case the decision is made on much less evidence than one would wish to have. It is all the evidence we do have and so must logically be accepted, but it should be understood that the two statements, that Paul wrote the four major Epistles and that the others come from six hands rest upon two different degrees of certainty corresponding to the evidence which is available.

ALTERNATIVE EXPLANATIONS OF THE EVIDENCE

When confronted by evidence of this kind many scholars at once react by offering explanations intended to preserve the Pauline authorship of all or most of the Epistles, though how scant the logical basis for this widely accepted position really is has been shown in Part One of this book.

The first suggestion is generally that Paul used an amanuensis. The rejoinder to this assertion is that this is something which we do not know. Another point which must be put is that no classical scholar will accept that the use of an amanuensis made any difference to a text. Homer was blind and must have used one but no Homeric scholar has felt obliged to defend the purity of the text against the amanuensis.

It must be borne in mind that until the Middle Ages reading and writing were voiced so that the modern contrast between a written and spoken style did not exist. To make this theory practicable the word "amanuensis" must be employed to cover not a scribe but a collaborator. This collaboration, it is asserted, must explain the differences between Galatians and Ephesians. The case of Josephus, examined earlier, is the one instance of a man who deliberately employed another man to improve his style. The difference could be detected, in large samples, but to explain the differences found in the Pauline Corpus some other explanation is necessary.

It is easy to show that the names attached to the Epistles themselves do not accommodate themselves to theories of collaborators. Paul's name alone stands on Ephesians, which he did not write; his name is coupled with that of Tertius on Romans which he did write, as far as stylistic analysis rather than penmanship is concerned.

And what of the statement of II Thessalonians 3: 17?

But would anyone argue thus unless he felt that the Pauline authorship had to be defended? Why should it be defended? It has never had any better foundation than the accretion of centuries of acceptance as the least troublesome assumption to make.

A second alternative explanation suggested is that Paul was a unique individual. This is usually put forward in the form that Paul was an exceptional man and the evidence that this was so is his experience on the Damascus Road. That this is told not by Paul but by the anonymous author of Acts is passed over. Paul himself classes his own experience with that of Peter, the twelve, and five hundred others. That his experience was unique in any but the personal sense of the word, Paul was himself anxious to deny.

However this theory is but one example of the class of theory which will explain all the differences which are shown to exist within the Pauline Corpus in terms of special circumstances. It is simpler if the adherents of this type of hypothesis just say that this is their axiomatic assumption and save us the trouble of reading their arguments which can only illustrate their assumptions.

It is quite possible to assert that Paul wrote all fourteen Epistles. To do this you have to put him in places where it is unlikely that he ever was and put him there at times which create chronological difficulties; you have to assume he had one set of unconscious habits when he wrote I and II Thessalonians, changed them half a dozen times with the changing circumstances of his imagined life, yet contrived to be consistent four times, in Romans, I and II Corin-

G

thians and Galatians, and twice, but at different levels, in I and II Thessalonians and I and II Timothy, and was unique in the four instances of Ephesians, Philippians, Colossians and Hebrews.

This is not impossible but the situation has more than a superficial resemblance to the times of Copernicus. It is possible that the earth stands still and all the planets go round it in an elaborate system of circles but the special and exceptional circumstances need to make the theory workable are so many that reason rebels. The theory that the earth moves is simpler and altogether more credible.

Just so can it be said that Paul might have written any number of Epistles from none to fourteen. But the number of exceptional circumstances needed to reconcile the evidence and the theory strains the credulity in all but the one case, when the hypothesis is that Paul wrote only the four major Epistles.

FURTHER EVIDENCE

If this hypothesis is true, that the author of Galatians also wrote Romans and I and II Corinthians, then supporting evidence should not be hard to find.

This will be discovered in two fields. The first field is the further analysis of stylistic habits. This is proceeding. More refined statistical techniques are being employed and must bring more detailed analysis. It is already clear that some investigations are likely to increase our knowledge of writers' habits. It is known, for example, that the proportion of nouns or verbs used by writers of Greek prose varies with circumstances and subject matter, but that the proportion of adjectives and adverbs is constant. The proportion of adjectives and adverbs—not the number of times the different adjectives and adverbs are used—is consistent for the four major Epistles.

Cumulative-sum techniques will show the periodic nature of habits and it has been shown by this method, that Ephesians, Philippians and Colossians are written by men with quite contrasting habits in their grouping of sentences.

A number of workers have now entered this field and results will soon appear in quantity.

The second approach is to look at the personal habits of Paul as he is now defined. This can be readily illustrated. In the four major Epistles are two hundred questions; they occur at the rate of twenty-six questions in every 1,500 words of text. In all the other Epistles there is but one question per 1,500 words. This habit of asking rhetorical questions is one which Paul might not share with any other author but that the rate is constant in the four Epistles and dramatically different in the others is evidence of a real similarity in the four and a real difference outside them. Another such habit is the Pauline manner of introducing quotations from the Old Testament, again uniform in the four major Epistles and quite different in the others.

Of course the literature of New Testament studies has many instances of such habits though they are not often organised to show the resemblance between the major Epistles and the contrast with the others. One of the most interesting is Professor John Knox who remarks that the collection for famine relief which Paul was organising loomed large in the apostle's mind and in the first four Epistles, then drops from sight. If Knox had then made the correct deduction about the authorship he could have gone on to assess the importance and function of the collection.

There can be only one fitting conclusion to an investigation of this kind, the reminder that the first scholar to argue that Paul was the author of the four major Epistles alone was F. C. Baur and the first scholar to show that Baur had objective grounds for his argument was Dr W. C. Wake.

Note:

The technical paper referred to on page 90 will be issued in April 1966. M. Levison, A. Q. Morton, W. C. Wake, "Some Statistical Features of the Pauline Epistles", *Journal of the Royal Philosophical Society*, July 1966.

PART THREE

CHAPTER EIGHT

MOSAIC OR MAN?

SINCE the thesis that Paul wrote only five of the New Testament Epistles flies in the face of the hypothesis on this subject which has been adopted by most British scholars, it may be worth reminding ourselves of the status of what is sometimes called "the consensus of scholarly opinion".

Majority opinion is only the opinion of the majority: there is nothing sacrosanct about it. It provides in the meantime a working hypothesis. So long as it is able to contain all the salient facts within its framework, it is the best of its kind. If the matter is one of probability, if, in the nature of the case, certainty is not within reach there and then, every hypothesis is open to question and may be superseded.

Many matters in New Testament criticism are of this kind. What are called "the assured results of scholarship" are simply the conclusions of the most reputable scholars up to the present and in the light of the facts and theories which hitherto have had a claim to be considered. But should new and relevant questions arise which make it necessary to challenge these "assured results", nothing can relieve us of the duty to allow the old and the new to fight it out. In these circumstances such considerations as the opinion of the majority, the time for which it has been held, the readjustments that might be necessary should it now be found wanting, count for nothing. The only question is: Which is truer?

The preliminary skirmishes in which a new theory is obliged to engage are of a stereotyped order. At first it encounters either ridicule or blank incredulity which takes the form of vociferous assertions that it cannot be true. The Bishop of Woolwich's initial reaction to this theory was: "No one seriously supposes that everyone has a unique style detectable like a fingerprint" (*Observer* 10 Nov. 63). No one? But no one a hundred years ago seriously supposed that everyone had a unique fingerprint. Did the bishop himself up to this point ever give a second thought to the detection of specific measurable characteristics of individual style?

All sorts of reasons, from the fact that the Epistles patently say they were written by Paul to learned arguments purporting to show homogeneous development of one man's thought throughout the whole range of the Corpus, are likely to be heaped across the path of the new theory. This is instinctive defence of the old against the new. It is unusual at this stage to find a forthright approach like that of Professor Evans who said: "Our reaction in London was to invite the operator of the computer to come and explain."

To destroy the thesis it would be necessary to do one of three things: (1) Demonstrate that the results of using this method are entirely fortuitous, or (2) Show that there is some special reason why the method which works for all other Greek prose is not applicable in the solitary instance of the Pauline Corpus, or (3) Prove that even if the method is sound, the mathematical calculations are wrong. There is no other way of demolishing it and the day is past when the hunches of literary critics or theological system-makers have any relevance to this kind of problem.

The next stage in opposition is to play down the importance of the results. Since the notorious F. C. Baur is the only one to have come to almost the same conclusion, and that by an entirely different process, there is little likelihood that much will be made of the argument, that even if it has to be conceded that the thesis is true, the results are not new. The work of Dr W. C. Wake was the first attempt to apply statistical theories to this problem. It was completely ignored by New Testament scholars.

We come to a more interesting stage when it is said that the effects of the thesis are negligible. The conclusions do not matter, make no difference, are of academic interest only. Rev. T. Corbishley, S.J., has an invincible position. "Even if it were proved conclusively that not one single Epistle was actually composed by the Apostle himself, this could make no difference to the church's attitude to their theological content." But then, what would? This Olympian indifference to evidence which does not serve the great design is a luxury scholars cannot afford.

These are the teething troubles of any new theory, mentioned only in passing. The purpose of this section is to show some of the effects that are likely to follow from the thesis that Paul wrote only five of the Epistles and to indicate broadly the kind of readjustments that must be made in our thinking about the apostle.

The statement of J. Weiss that the history of primitive Christianity is usually written as the history of St Paul is still near enough to the truth to indicate the commanding position the apostle holds in the church's conception of its own history and theology. If, therefore, our conception of Paul has to be modified, it is mere foolery to argue that this does not make any difference. Again, if the delimitation of the number of Paul's genuine letters does not affect our estimate of Paul's life and thought, a great deal of rot has been talked about the unique qualities of the spurious Epistles.

It may be that some people are not interested in enlarging their knowledge of Paul and early Christianity. They may believe with Father Corbishley that in all books fortunate enough to be included in the New Testament "divine inspiration is at work, operating through the human author, whoever he may have been". But we are interested in what can be known, not in specialised theories of inspiration.

The delineation of Paul's thought is important for two main reasons. First, there is the sheer fact that he fills a position in orthodox church history which otherwise would be blank. It is a position of primary importance since he is the earliest New Testament writer, and indeed the only one who gives a first-hand inside account of primitive Christianity.

Second, there are indications that in some significant respects he was not typical of the generation to which he belonged. His own beliefs, however statutory the standard interpretation of them became in later times, require to be known with some precision if we are to begin to understand the historical origins of Christianity.

Hence, except for purposes which have no relation to the quest for knowledge, it is naïve to treat the difficult questions of Paul's authorship as matters of no consequence.

It has been the misfortune of Christianity that for the most part its history has been written by theological historians while its theology has not been written by historical theologians. Christianity's claim to be a "historical" religion gave impetus to the interest in historical research. Its own history, however, has to a large extent remained segregated from the modern revolution in historical thinking. Christian writers too often have had little use for historical information unless it could be shaped for apologetic purposes.

At the same time the emphasis on tradition (to be distinguished from an emphasis on the historical) has been inordinately strong, for reasons we need not enumerate. Theologians have therefore inclined to believe that whatever historical foundations are necessary to traditional orthodoxy are well and truly laid.

The attitude has been that even if the "secular" historian would find no evidence on which to base a confident superstructure, it must be there; no warrant is needed for surmising its invisible presence. Few systematic theologians until recently have realised and admitted even to themselves the depth of ignorance that surrounds the early days of the church. They have taken it for granted that the Pauline

Corpus is sufficient guarantee of the continuous and progressive explication of the one faith from Pentecost to the early catholic period.

So long, therefore, as systematic theology is regarded as the master mason in the church, archaeologists, historians, exegetes are all cast as sub-contractors working for the theologians. The latter have no intention of being deprived of their traditional certainties and are predisposed to use every new piece of information in terms of their own theological needs. Hence the condescending attitude to history, the safeguards taken against uncomfortable shocks, the under-estimate of the consequences which historical criticism must entail.

If Paul did not write the bulk of the letters assigned to him, the traditional idea of Paul is unhistorical. It has been a useful mosaic, not a man. The pseudonymous letters can no longer be used as sources for Paul's own theology nor can they form part of the tenuous known link between the first days of Christianity and the death of the apostle. "Pauline" as signifying teaching congruent with the mind of Paul is no longer a useful adjective and "Deutero-Pauline" has lost its connotation.

The new thesis calls for a new interest in the distinctions that can be discerned within the corpus, recognising that the motives leading to their collection may have been more fortuitous and less deliberate and self-conscious than has been thought. It is time to get rid of the oppressive anxiety to discern unanimous testimony to current theological predilections in the whole of the New Testament, and also of the habit of mind which is predisposed to regard all diver-gencies in the New Testament as minimal and irrelevant.

The notion still obtains that a pristine deposit of faith, kerygma, Gospel, word of God, is presented in the documents of the New Testament as a whole and that this is the criterion by which all subsequent doctrine is evaluated and indeed controlled. The one original faith was preserved from adulteration and insulated from all but the most negligible influences of external historical factors till in due course it was set down definitely at Nicaea and Chalcedon.

If this is not overtly proclaimed today, it is still tacitly but firmly assumed by many historians of early Christian doctrine. The great creeds are regarded as the final and authoritative formulation of what had been given at the beginning. It is contended, for instance, that the church was always trinitarian, though unready to give adequate expression to this at first; it had always believed in the homoousian and the two natures, though the time was not ripe for declaring this till 325 and 451.

The difficulties of this assumption began to be evident with the rise of historical criticism. Even while it was still believed that the Pauline Corpus was largely the work of Paul, the line from Pentecost through Paul to post-apostolic Christianity became increasingly difficult to trace. As the Pauline Corpus was pulled up to join hands with post-apostolic theology, a gap opened between it and the primitive tradition, and vice versa. The blanket was too short for the bed.

At first it appeared most likely that Paul's distinctive role was to Hellenise the Gospel. Particularly in the study of the Captivity Epistles did it seem that "Paul" had made himself and his Gospel at home in the setting of Graeco-Roman philosophy and religion. Even in Romans, scholars like Pfleiderer found a basic agreement in ideas of "flesh", "spirit" and "conscience", while others considered that his teaching on Baptism and the Lord's Supper owed more to the pagan world than to Judaism.

Meantime it began to become apparent that if the Hellenisation of the Gospel were in fact due to the thinking of the apostle, he was by this much the less in rapport with the original preaching of the first believers, not to say of Jesus himself. They were Jewish in upbringing and thought and to them many of the ideas common to Graeco-Roman culture were nothing short of idolatrous.

Schweitzer spoke of the "great and still undischarged task" which he put in the form of the question: "How could the doctrinal system of Paul arise on the basis of the life and work of Jesus and the beliefs of the primitive community and how did the early Greek theology arise out of Paulinism?"

And yet on the basis of the "Hauptbriefe" it was possible to maintain that Paul was in fact a Hebrew of the Hebrews. Those, therefore, who were most concerned to secure the link between Paul and the primitive church were found to make more use of the first four letters and to let the Hellenistic side look after itself. They discovered the distinctive "Pauline" theology in Galatians and Romans interpreted in post-Reformation terms of justification by faith, a Judaic doctrine of atonement, sanctification through being in Christ—rather than in the speculative soteriology of Colossians. But they could suggest no satisfactory way of harmonising the two except by postulating that Paul's mind encompassed both extremes with equal ease and authority.

In 1872 Lüdemann found in the Pauline letters two anthropologies and two doctrines of redemption—one Jewish and the other dualistic. He argued that Galatians knows only the first while the second belongs to Colossians and the later years of Paul's life. Pfleiderer recognised the two strains and asserted that they held equal importance for Paul who was quite unaware of the inconsistency. The controversy on this matter involved such names as Reuss, Ménégoz and Sabatier. But, as Schweitzer remarks, in this period there is "much assertion and little proof". There was much confusion between theological and historical possibilities.

The question of the capacity of Paul's mind to comprehend or excogitate the whole gamut of doctrine from Galatians to Ephesians (to say nothing of the Pastorals) became one of considerable importance. In this way alone could the transition from primitive belief to early catholic theology be demonstrably authenticated. Doctrines scarcely to be discerned in the early Epistles are "fully articulated" in the later. Could it be shown that within the mind of one apostolic man there took place this kind of development? If so, the route from the primitive confession of Jesus as Messiah, whose parousia is imminent, to Nicaea and Chalcedon was thereby hallowed.

Because the area to be covered was considerable, only a mind of unique and extraordinary capacity could traverse it. Hence the increasing attention to the dramatic and revelatory nature of Paul's personal experience on the Damascus road, a factor first emphasised by Holtzmann. This encounter became the invincible explanation of Paul's thought and ability to carry out within his own mind a gigantic, not to say miraculous, feat of elucidation and reinterpretation. This feat at once preserved the original deposit and made it acceptable to an alien culture.

It was Wrede who brought sanity into the picture by showing that Paul must have had Messianic beliefs before he became convinced that Jesus was Messiah.

Christianity was undoubtedly Hellenised and this means change. But that it happened in the mind of a solitary man and in the space of thirty years does not follow. The theory that the Christian faith was given once for all, that it remained essentially the same by a providential process of development which involved no alteration that was not marginal, that it enjoyed divine immunity from historical contingency, and that Paul stands sponsor for the early and crucial period of its deposition is not tenable.

Two options remain for those to whom this conclusion is insupportable. They must find retreat with Father Corbishley or with those who erect the unity of the New Testament into a divinely revealed dogma, an ethereal doctrine of the church or an unhistorical doctrine of the New Testament.

Of recent years it has become more than ever obvious that the road through the Pauline Corpus does not lead directly to a consecrated destination in the great councils of the church. The factors that have influenced this conclusion are first, the new emphasis since Weiss and Schweitzer on the eschatological character of early Christianity, and second, the intensive study of Rabbinic Judaism.

Schweitzer maintained that it was not possible to rest content with a notion of Paul and his theology which solved its problems by attributing a magnanimous inconsistency to the mind of the apostle. He concluded that the author of Romans, Galatians, I and II Corinthians was not the author of Colossians, Ephesians and the Pastorals, though he found no reason to exclude Philippians and I Thessalonians. His portrait of the apostle is consequently one of the few which show us a man of undoubtedly remarkable qualities in a credible historical setting. Paul was a Jew who thought and reasoned as a Jew and whose relation to Hellenism was neither native nor obsequious.

More recently the studies of W. D. Davies and H. J. Schoeps have reinforced the same conclusion. In his immensely erudite *Paul and Rabbinic Judaism* Davies has made out an exhaustive case to show that "Paul belonged to the mainstream of first-century Judaism, and that elements in his thought, which are often labelled as Hellenistic, might well be derived from Judaism".

Davies was able to do this while regarding all the Pauline Corpus, excluding Hebrews, as material for Paul's theology. His greatest difficulties, as might be expected, arose from the Captivity Epistles. It is not without significance that he refers nearly four times as often to the first four letters as to all the others together.

It would seem therefore that at the present time the emphasis is on the common ground which Paul shares with the early church. We shall turn to this in the next chapter. Meantime what has been happening at the other end?

Historians of Christian doctrine at the turn of the century, such as Harnack and Loofs, were perplexed by the fact that there was no natural line between "Paul" and the post-apostolic age. Even those fathers at the beginning of the early catholic era who seemed to be most indebted to the Pauline literature were not at home with the most distinctive doctrines of the apostle. Thus Harnack wrote: "When one comes to write the history of the Early Church, the difficulty is that it is not in terms of the most obvious phenomenon of the Apostolic period, namely Paulinism, that the consequent development is to be understood" (*History of Dogma*, Vol. 1, p. 18).

The post-apostolic period does not show the kind of indebtedness to the "Pauline" type of doctrine that the traditional theory of development of doctrine requires. There is an "unconscious deterioration", a "smoothing down", a "minimising" of the characteristic features and the growth of a legalistic impulse which overpowers the dynamic quality of the Pauline Gospel. This kind of modification was thought to be due to a resurgence of Jewish christian influence mediated by the Old Testament (Harnack), or to the compromise worked out between Pauline and Petrine Christianity (Baur, Schwegler), or to the inability of the Hellenistic Christians to understand the place and use of the Old Testament in the Christian church (Ritschl). These possibilities have since been examined and found insufficient. The conclusion seems well founded that the phenomenon is not due to the impact of some external factor but to an internal change.

This was originally proposed by Schweitzer and is taken up by M. Werner. Both find the solution in the progressive failure of the expectation of the parousia. This factor was so central to primitive Christianity that any change here would be reflected in the ethos and teaching of the time. Ignatius and Justin do not turn to Paul. His age is not theirs and the expectation of the parousia is not constitutive of their faith as it was of his.

Werner summarises the process in this paragraph: "However, the *whole* of the first generation of the faithful died out, without having experienced the fulfilment of the Pauline promise, thus proving that it was certainly not the privileged community of the Saints of the Last Days. This meant in turn that the Apostolic Age was not, in terms of the primitive Christian expectation, the beginning of the final epoch. But with the collapse of this *presupposition* of the definite significance of the Apostolic Age went the eschatological significance of the Death and Resurrection of Jesus. This change of things proved itself in effect to be the turning-point of that subsequent crisis of Christianity which, starting in the Post-Apostolic period, led, by virtue of the process of Hellenisation, to early Catholicism" (*The Formation of Christian Dogma*, p. 25).

However bitter a pill it may be in some quarters, the limitation of Paul's actual letters to five corroborates the need for a more openminded approach to Schweitzer and the "Konsequent-Eschatologische" school. Hitherto they have been known in this country only to be controverted and studied only that their conclusions might be by-passed.

CHAPTER NINE

THE MIND OF PAUL

THERE is a devotional use of Scripture which is relatively independent of knowledge about the how and why of the Scripture's existence. For many, the words of the twenty-third Psalm need no commentary and John 14 is complete without exegesis. It is true that a great deal is tacitly assumed, probably that David was the author in the first example and that Jesus did say what appears in John 14. Any piece of literature has a quasi-life of its own once it has been created. It may serve a purpose as far as the reader is concerned which is unrelated and even foreign to the writer's intention.

"One of the signs of great religious thought and great religious literature is that both of them are capable of bearing so many meanings which were not in the minds of their authors. Succeeding generations have read the Psalms and have found in them a quintessence of piety without being concerned with the precise significance and contexts in which, over the centuries, these poems were written. The works of Plato became of religious significance when they were read five centuries after his death in a sense largely different from that which he had probably put upon them. So it is with Paul" (A. D. Nock, *St Paul*, p. 20).

In such cases the reader is using what is written as a means of supplying his own personal need at the time and there is no law against this. He gets out what he puts in. But he is in trouble if he begins to say he is doing something else, such as understanding the mind of the author. We distinguish therefore between using a piece of literature and understanding the mind of the writer, recognising, of course, that the latter may lead to a more accurate and more worthwhile form of the first.

How are these two attitudes affected in cases where the document has been assigned to the wrong author? Obviously its use as a sounding-board for the reader's personal devotional needs is not impaired; but understanding the mind of the author is now upset. For example, nothing can affect the use of Colossians if it is assumed to be a vehicle of divine truth irrespective of who wrote it. The argument is moved to another area, namely, what permits us to make such an assumption. But if Colossians has been taken as reflecting the mind of Paul and it is now agreed to be not by Paul, this perforce has an important bearing on the business of understanding the mind of the apostle.

The question here is not how the letters of the Pauline Corpus help individual Christians. This can have different answers in different ages and for different people. It is a question which is important for each reader individually and can be answered only by himself. But the general and objective question is, What kind of man was Paul and how did he come to say and write what he did?

The thesis that Paul wrote only five of the Epistles, while it will not affect the devotional use of the rest, will be bound to affect the understanding of the mind of Paul. He is no longer the man who wrote seven, ten or thirteen New Testament letters but the man who wrote Romans, I and II Corinthians, Galatians and Philemon. This is a simplification of the main question, even if it raises other questions whose answers may at present elude us. The most obvious are: Who wrote the other letters and when and why were they written?

A five-Epistle Paul delivers us from the gross incongruities inseparable from the attempt to find the mind of Paul, one man, at the centre of all the Pauline letters. This was possible, theoretically, only on the basis of an assumption prefabricated to suit the situation. One form of this assumption is stated by Deissmann as follows: "Paul had room in his personality for contradictions which would have hopelessly shattered a small man" (*Paul*, p. 60). This sounds well and may be true. But Deissmann has made the statement because he regarded all the Epistles as genuine and he thinks that only a mind which is capable of comprehending shattering contradictions could have written them all. If not Paul, who then?

But when Käsemann says that Ephesians and Colossians are intelligible "only from a mode of interpretation which takes Gnosticism fully into account", it is no longer necessary to wonder how this was possible to the writer of Galatians. There is no longer any need to trace in the mind of one man what W. L. Knox speaks of as "a progressive adaptation of the Christian message to the general mental outlook of the Hellenistic world".

The mind of Paul is not a cyclopaedia of first-century theology. It centres upon a group of homogeneous ideas to be found in the five letters he wrote. These ideas are large and pregnant enough to admit him to the company of the master thinkers. Those who have persuaded themselves that the speculations of Ephesians and Colossians are the crown of Paul's thinking, just because they have believed Paul wrote them and for no other reason, should not find it difficult to change their minds.

The point is that one obstacle to arriving at a true estimate of the mind of Paul has been removed. It is no longer necessary to argue that since Paul wrote most of the letters, his mind must be such as is capable of this feat, however incomprehensible.

A second obstacle has been the use to which orthodoxy has put the letters, namely as the touchstone of pure doctrine. This has naturally resulted in a conception of Paul which is a theological abstraction. Not without cause did Deissmann call us to "come back from the paper Paul of our western libraries, from the Germanised, dogmatised, modernised, stilted Paul, to the historic Paul" (*op. cit.*, p. 4). But the "historic Paul" was already lost to view a long time before there were any Western libraries.

There was no man who wrote the Pauline Epistles in such a way that they could be used as the source and test of sound doctrine for ever after. The interpretation of Paul's letters depends on historical insight rather than on theological erudition. The ability to judge what is possible within a specific historical context takes priority over the skill to weave theological data into a system of doctrine. Since the church has interested itself almost exclusively in the theology of Paul as the explication of a divine plan of human salvation, the persona of Paul the theologian has obliterated Paul the man. But the theologian is not to be seen except as a travesty unless we see the man as a real man in his own real situation.

What we need is not only as much reliable information as possible about the activities of Paul but a credible context for his life and thought. This depends on knowing what could happen or be thought and why, more than on knowing what is reported to have happened on the assumption that Paul was and is a mouthpiece of timeless theological truth.

The mind of Paul is not therefore to be found by an exposition of his letters designed to elicit their relevance to the twentieth century, still less by an exposition of letters which he did not write, but by an understanding of the rise of Christianity of which his story is part.

Our ignorance of primitive Christianity is an ignorance of Paul and conversely our ignorance of Paul is an ignorance of primitive Christianity, simply because Paul's letters alone are extant as personal testimony from that period. We are fortunate to have these but unfortunate to have no more than these.

The five letters are written by a man who is convinced he has a unique role in a unique movement. This arises directly out of the letters themselves. They are first-hand testimony about the beginnings of the Christian church. They are cardinal both for our knowledge of the life and thought of the apostle and also for that of the

H

church. Neither the Gospels nor Acts, however valuable as ancillary material when rightly assessed, have the same indigenous quality.

This does not mean that these five letters may be used forthwith as a transcript of the early days of the church or of the mind of Paul. No document has this quality. Every document is a witness to be questioned, not an authority to be deferred to. The picture of the first days in these letters is given through Paul's eyes. It is different from that which would have been given in letters written by Peter or James. Similarly, the mind of Paul revealed in these letters is such as only Paul himself would reveal. It is as liable to subjective and subconscious bias as any other biographical material is bound to be. This is another reason why historical insight is of such importance.

It is clear therefore that a five-Epistle Paul requires not only or first of all a reassessment of Paul's theology. It requires a fresh look at the historical fact of the rise of Christianity as reflected in these five letters. These witness to an unprecedented movement in which the author believes himself to have a place no one but he can fill. Fortunately the subject of Christian Origins has been receiving renewed attention in our time, but it is still theological speculation rather than historical research that has pride of place.

At this point there arises a question of methodology. The movement and the man, Christianity and the apostle, are bound together in the letters. Knowledge of the one is relevant to the understanding of the other. It is not possible to separate the two if we begin from the letters themselves and yet the letters are our most important data for the early church.

The only reliable procedure is to begin from the general nature of the period as it is known in other sources that give genuine information. To begin from a notion of the theology of Paul and surmise a context for it is to run the danger of losing contact with actuality. This is commonly the fault of Pauline studies ever since the rise of historical criticism. It is the reason why there are so few authentic books about Paul. The problem is similar to that of the Gospels where form criticism is used to give a setting for the words and deeds of Jesus. In fact only some understanding of the historical setting can give a milieu for the work of the form critic.

From this point of view the only reliable method is to start from the known characteristics of the age, from the work of Schürer and his successors, from the recognition that, as Schoeps says, the period from the apocalypse of Daniel (168–4 B.C.) to Bar Kokhba (A.D. 135) is one of uninterrupted eschatological tension and that eschatology forms the greatest block of material in the thought world of Paul (H. J. Schoeps, *Paul*, pp. 40–6).

The Christian movement is pre-eminently an eschatological movement in its origins. It is characterised more particularly by the belief that the Messiah is Jesus and that his parousia is at hand. The five Epistles are written within this schema. This is the common ground which Paul occupies with the first believers and on which he finds his own conception of his life-work. On this there is no divergence of opinion though the conclusions to be drawn therefrom are subject to controversy as between Paul and others. The point is well made that the quarrel was not over something which Paul had added to the basic belief, such as would justify a charge of Hellenisation, for instance. It was over the kind of consequences which flow from the basic belief itself, in particular with reference to the Gentiles, the Law and the nature of the period in which believers are now living.

What is the likelihood that Paul's conception of the significance of Jesus' death differed from that of the original believers? Is there any doubt that his notion of the part played by the Law was different from theirs? Was his teaching about the resurrection, as an experience of believers, shared by them? Did he make more of the present, being-in-Christ, than others?

The range and power of Paul's mind are to be discovered in answer to such questions. They have nothing to do with alien currents of thought and everything to do with profound intellectual curiosity arising from utter commitment to the movement through personal dedication to Christ as Lord.

In recent years there has been a tendency (created by theological necessity) to minimise the probability that Paul worked out the consequences of his Messianic faith to different conclusions from those prevalent at Jerusalem. This has been an aspect of the desire to find the Gospel not in particular Scriptures but in the New Testament as a whole, the present-day substitute for verbal inspiration. Both its method and its effects are suspect. It professes to be able to educe the "pre-Pauline" from the letters of Paul (how many pre-Pauline Christians were there?) and it results in reducing the apostle to a mouthpiece of what is called "pre-Pauline theology".

Professor A. M. Hunter, for example, here follows Héring, Cullmann, Jeremias and others. Using most of the Epistles as his data, he finds pre-Pauline hymns embedded in the letters, maintains that faith, hope and charity are a primitive Christian triad, that the idea of Christ as the Second Adam was not original with Paul, that many of his hortatory sections derive from paraenetic tradition current at the time, that his use of the Old Testament is inherited from earlier believers, and that indeed "Much of Paul's theology is not the fruit of his own speculation but goes back to pre-Pauline thought about Jesus" (See *Paul and His Predecessors*). This is a long way from Holtzmann and the revelation on Damascus road. But how can it be proved that this body of pre-Pauline thought about Jesus exists outside the Pauline Corpus?

Hunter's intention is "to clear St Paul of the charge of being an arch-innovator". Whether the author of Galatians would wish such a service is at least doubtful—especially when the cost is counted. Hunter does this as Lytton Strachey *malgré lui*, reducing the apostle to a snapper-up of other people's notions. The Paul of the letters is at pains to deny indebtedness, even to the pillars of the church, but Hunter assures us "we can lay too much emphasis" on what Paul has to say on this score. Paul it appears has received credit for what really belongs to nameless earlier believers. Not that we should blame Paul for this. It is all the fault of the scoundrel Marcion who has preserved so many of Paul's letters!

One wonders if Dr Hunter approves when the same technique is turned on the teaching of Jesus. Are Klausner and Bultmann also among the prophets?

It is neither necessary nor possible to maintain that Paul's originality involved no indebtedness to predecessors. Hunter may be near the mark in some of his examples though certainly wrong in those based on pseudonymous material. Even where his case seems strong, however, is the matter crucial and is it provable that Paul's indebtedness was to members of the early Christian society? But the main objection is that Professor Hunter makes his case in order to serve a confessedly dogmatic and apologetic purpose and is not prepared to allow the possibility that Paul's interpretation of the Gospel could differ significantly from that of the Jerusalem apostles. The historian in him is compelled to play acolyte to the theologian.

The genuine letters reveal one thing very clearly—that as far as we know and are ever likely to know, *pace* Dr C. H. Dodd, Paul was the first believer in realised eschatology. This may account for some of the main differences between himself and those at Jerusalem. For him first of all as far as our records are concerned the New Age had actually come into being to some extent in practical terms. This conviction gave him a distinctive view of the significance of the crucifixion, the Law, the resurrection and the mission to the Gentiles. It faced him with the problem of what happens to a New Age man who dies before the parousia. He proceeded to solve it without reference to his mentors at Jerusalem.

It is the same distinctive view, no longer tenable when the first generation died out and still the parousia had not arrived, which made it impossible for the post-apostolic age to adopt Paul's characteristic theological convictions, even when they felt obliged to use Paul's phraseology.

The mind of Paul is not the apotheosis of the minds of unknown first believers. It cannot be reduced to mediocrity without making nonsense of the letters and of the development of Christian doctrine. Again, it is not a compendium of the whole range of opinions from the primitive confession that Jesus is Messiah to the cosmological speculations of a Gnosticised Christianity. It is the mind revealed in the five letters he wrote, a mind which is nothing if not powerful, creative and independent, the mind of a man pioneering his own thoughts about God's will and work in the world he knows.

CHAPTER TEN

PAUL IN ACTS

BROADLY speaking the church has taken its conception of Paul's theology from the Epistles, of his life from Acts. But while the writer of Acts shows little insight into Paul's mind, the letters have something to say of his life which must be regarded as authoritative. In particular, there is the autobiographical section in Galatians 1: 11–16 which tells a different story from the relative sections of Acts. This raises questions about the trustworthiness of the picture of Paul given us by Acts.

There is no denying the importance of Acts as the only "history" of the early period. But it is not to be taken as it stands, and the more closely it is examined, the less possible is it to treat it as history in the modern sense.

It is useless to rake over the arguments on discrepancies between Acts and Galatians. The particular points have been debated endlessly. More accurately, ceaseless attempts have been made to harmonise the two. The only reasonable conclusion is that the first-hand evidence of Paul himself must be preferred to the second-hand version in Acts—unless we are prepared to believe that when Paul puts himself on oath he is not to be trusted.

We have, fortunately, another test which can be applied to Acts when it is remembered that the complete work is Luke–Acts. In the first volume of his work we are able to see how the parts were put together and what use was made of the sources at the compiler's command. From his use of Mark and Q and in comparison with the other synoptic Gospel we are able to form some estimate of his method of using sources and the extent to which he is faithful to them.

Briefly, the result of this examination has been as follows. He does not mind changing words here and there to suit his own literary taste or even to give a somewhat different nuance to the narrative. He is quite capable of selecting material to suit his own point of view and appears to have certain favourite interests for which he makes room. Thus he gives preference to the part played by women, to stories of domestic life, to the poor. He is also partial to miracles which feature visions, angels and voices, noticeably in the new beginning (Luke 1–2) and the post-crucifixion narratives, where there is no evidence that he was bound by written sources. He is inclined to alter details in stories and sayings and to rearrange the order of events to give better expression to his own views of their meaning and importance. This is to say that he is not content to copy and has a viewpoint of his own.

Bultmann has observed, "Luke's chief interest is literary. His ambition was to write his story in a way that would impress even his cultured readers, and he had a special concern to reproduce the right τάξις i.e. an evidently historical sequence (1: 1–4)" (*The History of the Synoptic Tradition*, pp. 365, 366).

The "great interpolation" (9: 51–18: 14) gives an order and sequence to the journey to Jerusalem which also makes room for material not attached by tradition to any particular place or time. This order and sequence as far as can be known have no support from the point of view of historical verisimilitude. Today, however, we might be content to say that one of the compiler's chief interests is literary.

The key question here is asked by Professor John Knox (*Chapters in a Life of Paul*, p. 15). "Why should we suppose that Luke, who can be shown to have had meagre sources and to have made independent, although admittedly careful and responsible, use of those he had when he wrote the first volume of his work, had adequate sources and simply recorded what they clearly told him when he wrote his second volume? The fortuitous absence of parallel accounts does not justify us in being less critical of Acts than we are forced to be of Luke."

Criticism of Acts has usually taken the form of defence of its trustworthiness and of its Lucan authorship. The two are presumed to stand or fall together since although the Lucan authorship would not of itself be a guarantee of its trustworthiness, it would make it relatively more likely, especially as it is also assumed that Luke was the companion of Paul. However, in the case of Luke-Acts no claim to Lucan authorship is embedded in the volumes. The sparse facts of Luke's life are taken from Acts on the assumption that he is the author of the "we-sections" and from a reference in Colossians.

Tradition has had plenty of scope in this instance. Luke was and was not one of the apostles. He was a missionary in one or other or all of these countries—Italy, Greece, Dalmatia, Gaul, Bithynia, Africa—"in fact over all the known world". He was a painter of considerable merit besides being a doctor. He was also a bishop, both at Alexandria and at Ephesus. He died in his bed at Thebes in Boeotia and at Ephesus. He also died as a martyr, being executed at

Alexandria and slaughtered along with 169 brothers at Rome. Whether the name Luke is more than a name or not, the fact that Luke–Acts is attributed to him seems to be evidence that it was not written by anyone prominent in the apostolic church, or at least that it was not known that this was so.

The ruthless approach to Acts is by way of the fact that the book is compounded of wonders more extravagant than any to be found elsewhere in the New Testament and comparable only with those in positively apocryphal Gospels and Acts. A book of this size which contains a score of major miracles including bodily assumption, angelic interventions and punitive sorcery does not immediately inspire confidence in its historicity. When the miraculous is so prominent and so evidently congenial to the author's mind, it is reasonable to suspect that either the author has heightened the thaumaturgic element himself, or it has been well developed before it reached him and he was predisposed to receive it. In either case the author or compiler is at some remove from the events he records. The exigencies of credulity, if allowed to shape history, make it difficult for the author to find a point of rest beyond which the readiness to believe is exhausted.

It is not reasonable to dismiss an author simply because what we call the miraculous was part of his everyday composite view of the course of history, even if it is only the history of a particular movement. But if it is found that he cannot think of his subject without assuming that the miraculous is the history, then we may consider whether this fact forces us to believe that he might on occasion sacrifice something for the sake of a good story. The compiler who gives us a collection of material about the first days of the church and introduces it with the bodily ascension and the Pentecost story in chapter 2 is such an author.

The second obvious factor is the amount of padding out that is done, mainly in speeches. If we consider those by Peter, the two speeches by Paul recounting the already-told events on the Damascus road, the long anomalous oration by Stephen, and add to this the detailed account of the sea voyage and shipwreck, a fair proportion of the book is accounted for. This material, together with the miracles, makes it possible to say that Acts is a book of dramatic events and magniloquent speeches strung together on a thin chord which may be largely of the compiler's own weaving.

Morton and Macgregor refer to "the prolixity of the later chapters" as one of the three main problems in the structure of Acts. "The book ends abruptly with Paul awaiting his trial. One would give much to read the sequels. Yet the last few chapters contain much repetitious argument and describe events in greater detail than one finds in similar events described in the early chapters of the book. This problem is conveniently summarised in the story of Paul's conversion. The story first appears in IX: 1–19, thirty lines of Souter's (Greek) text. It is repeated in the improbable setting of the aftermath of a riot, in XXII: 3–30, where it fills thirty-five lines of Souter. It appears again as part of Paul's defence before Agrippa and now takes up forty lines of Souter's text. The story is not only repeated, it is progressively enlarged, and with all this increase, little new information is being given" (*The Structure of Luke and Acts:* Morton & Macgregor, 1964, p. 24).

The padding out suggests that the author did not want his book to end except where it did, with Paul at Rome still preaching the Gospel. There may be several reasons for this. Nothing may have been known about Paul's last days, either by the author or by any of his contemporaries, beyond the fact that he was taken to Rome and imprisoned. Some apologetic or theological aim would not have been served by an account of Paul's execution at Roman hands, presuming the author knew it had taken place. He may have refrained from recounting the martyrdom of Paul when he had no comparable story of Peter whose speeches and miracles in Acts correspond so deliberately with those of Paul.

But the sheer literary interest of the compiler may be sufficient explanation. He evidently took delight in composing speeches suited to different occasions and had some pride in his ability in this direction. He may even go the length of deliberately making occasion for them by creating entirely fictitious settings. It is clear that preaching, working miracles and suffering persecution are signs for him that the Gospel is making progress in the world. How much of the history he knew but omitted in order to make room for his main interests and enforce his thesis is unknown.

The difference of opinion between Paul and those at Jerusalem is dealt with in such a way as to imply it is merely a matter of administration. Whether he knew of its existence and mistook its import, or knew nothing at all of it, or deliberately relegated it, we certainly should now prefer that it had been treated historically, even at the expense of some of the orations. The compiler is too far from it to have any worthwhile opinion, or not a good enough historian to have seen that it was important, or more anxious to influence the present than portray the past, in spite of his obvious desire to be taken as a kind of historian.

His distance from the event is shown in the fact that he can attempt a synoptic view of the apostolic age as a movement inaugurated by spiritual baptism and continuing the life of the Master through apostles who preach, heal and suffer persecution. C. K. Barrett says that "In the Gospel his purpose was to tell the story of the Founder of the Church; this set the pattern for Acts, in which he showed how the Spirit of Jesus moulded men in His likeness, and used them in the continuation of His work" (*Luke the Historian in Recent Study*, p. 61).

The writer of such a book is not simply a naïve chronicler of events. For some reason or reasons he thinks the story worth telling. The question arises to what extent this fact shapes his history or how anxious he is to produce history rather than propaganda. To all appearance the writer of Luke–Acts and of Acts in particular has a strong desire to be regarded as a historian.

In his second volume he is doing what has not yet been done, presenting a record of the historical events related to the growth of the church. This is to say that *prima facie* his intention is that of a historian. How good he is at his job depends probably on his sources. But it also depends on the ethos of his time and the extent to which he consciously adopts attitudes to his subjects which are latent in the period to which he belongs.

All this makes it difficult to say when he is recounting the past, when he is assuming a conventional attitude to the past, and whether he is at times imposing his own view on the past, with the intention of fostering a particular interpretation which will be useful for some purpose at the time of writing.

The interpreter of Acts for his part must beware of reading into the work motives which were not present to the mind of the writer, however plausible they may appear in the light of subsequent events. It is tempting, for instance, to find in Luke–Acts a conscious attempt to deal with the problems of Gnosticism and eschatology. The author, it is said, ignores the former and transfers interest in the latter to the church as a continuing historical society. Just as the Pastorals and the Johannine literature provide their own definite attitudes to those two post-apostolic questions so, it is argued, does Luke–Acts.

The author of Luke–Acts shows no familiarity with Gnostic thought. But this is not the same as saying that he deliberately ignored it and believed that was how to treat it. He is familiar with the parousia expectation. But it is hindsight that suggests that his conception of the church is intended to be a make-weight to the delay of the parousia.

These motives might be consciously present to writers like the authors of the Pastorals and "John". But if Luke–Acts is consciously intended as history to some degree, this fact weights against their presence in Acts. Dr Conzelmann's *Die Mitte der Zeit* admirably sets Luke–Acts in a credible historical context from a point of view further down the stream of history, but the question remains whether the author of Luke–Acts was himself aware of the solutions his work might afford to the theological problems of his own or a later time.

If we wish to take the author of Acts seriously as a historian, our attention is more profitably directed to what has been called the mythopoeic function of historiography. Livy, Tacitus and Polybius frankly pen their histories with the intention of glorifying the achievements of Rome. Misrepresentation arises in their case not only from ignorance and error but also by design related to what are thought to be the proper interests of a historian.

Here it may be in place to quote P. G. Walsh (*Livy, His Historical Aims and Methods*, p. 109). "Livy's moral and patriotic preoccupations led him to depict a series of leaders as the embodiment of the Stoic virtues of prudence, justice, courage and moderation, and of other virtues which the Roman tradition extolled. In these characterisations Livy has allowed his pursuit of edifying examples to take preference over a truthful account, not merely by distortion of emphasis, but even by supression of unpalatable facts." The preoccupations of the compiler of Acts are now beginning to receive more detailed attention.

The more we emphasise the thought of "Luke" as a historian, the less possible is it to believe that his conception of the historian's function was that of simply recording the past. To put the matter in other words, the expectation that in Acts we have history simply as chronicle is not feasible. We are well aware today that no such history can be written and it is factually impossible to see the events of Acts as transcripted from life.

Recent work on Acts since Dibelius' *Studies in the Acts of the Apostles* has begun to get to grips with the mind of the compiler. Haenchen, for instance, says that whereas formerly Acts was studied for information about the apostolic age, it is now being studied as a work of art. To appreciate it we need to understand the principles on which it was composed and the theology of the compiler. While Haenchen means by "principles of its composition" the personal viewpoint of the compiler, Macgregor and Morton have shown that sheer physical conditions, such as available space, contribute to the total impression the book conveys.

This is not the place to deal with the characteristics of the compiler of Acts in detail, but the present trend is increasingly damaging to the historical reliability of Acts, even if we concede the compiler's right to be regarded as a historian in his own age. It is now becoming necessary to say of Acts, as has been said of the Gospels, that we are in the presence of preaching in the form of history. The writer is in fact, whatever may have been his intention, more absorbed in his preaching than in his history.

Whether, for example, the ascension, the day of Pentecost, the preaching and miracles attributed to Peter ever took place, may not be decided on the basis of the text of Acts. In fact may never be decided at all. The compiler of Acts is an unforthcoming witness who is not convinced that what we would like to know is of any consequence.

When we come to particular facts that may be checked by parallel accounts, the weight of evidence is against Acts. The reference in the Gamaliel speech to Theudas is a chronological blunder. If Acts here follows Josephus, the book is removed to a date which many church historians and theologians till recently have thought it vital to resist.

In Acts, Paul is represented as persecuting in Jerusalem and Judaea. He himself says he was not known to Christians there till some time later. In Acts, Paul's visits to Jerusalem are irreconcilable with those given in Galatians. Acts shows Paul subordinate to the earlier apostles centred at Jerusalem. Paul himself vigorously asserts his independence. Acts shows him as a powerful orator and knows nothing of him as a letter-writer; Corinthians says he was poor as a speaker but an effective writer.

The personal attitude of the compiler to Paul himself is ambiguous. It is as if he would have wished it had not been Paul who achieved so great a reputation for the spread of Christianity. But since this is the case and since the rise and growth of Christianity is his theme, he must give Paul credit, but not without restraint.

The status of Paul is that which he wins as a missionary in contrast to what Peter and the others have by grace of the fact that they actually lived with Jesus. Only twice in the book is Paul given the status of an apostle, and that almost by inadvertence. In 14: 4 there is a division of opinion in Iconium over Paul and Barnabas and "part held with the Jews and part with the apostles". In 14: 14 when preparations are being made to sacrifice to the missionaries as gods, the narrative continues, "which when the apostles, Barnabas and Paul, heard of, they rent their clothes, etc." The title of "apostle" in Acts is primarily reserved for those who had seen the Lord (the condition to be met in appointing a successor to Judas), not for missionaries.

Paul himself says he saw the Lord. But in the three accounts of the

Damascus road incident, it is not once indicated that he did. The compiler seems to belong to a time or circle in which the apostles were being limited in number to those thought to have been particularly appointed by Jesus and qualified by sight of him after his resurrection. Paul was not reckoned one. Since this was one of the contentious issues between Paul and those at Jerusalem and his claim was admitted later by the church at large, the attitude of the compiler of Acts is unlikely to be unintentional.

If we require further evidence of this ambivalent attitude to the apostle, it is found in the desire of the writer to show an orderly development of Christianity, at the expense of subordinating Paul to the church at Jerusalem. This he does in spite of Paul's own categorical denial that this was the relationship.

Paul, in Acts, preaches first only in synagogues. He has part in the beginning of work among Gentiles, though not before Peter, and only at the invitation of others. Not in immediate consequence of a divine commission does he go to the Gentile world, nor does he preach as a pioneer following his own gleam. He is there by co-option and at the instance of authority, not as an apostle but as a missionary. Acts appears to know nothing of Paul's correspondence, so that deliberate mishandling of history may be out of the question. But the writer has taken over, and apparently wishes to propagate, the view of orderly and centralised evangelism. This view had become necessary in face of the post-apostolic situation of the church, the beginnings of what has been called "early catholicism".

It was F. C. Baur who first made it clear that the attitude of Paul to those at Jerusalem and vice versa was important for understanding Paul's life and thought and for the early history of the church. "He started with a great fact, a fact that put to confusion the pious notion—seventeen hundred years old—that the Apostolic Age was like the Saviour's garment, free from seams, a paradise of high-tempered peace" (H. S. Nash).

In his essay on parties in the church at Corinth, Baur brought the conflict into prominence and shattered the time-worn legend of harmonious apostolic co-operation. He saw the significance of this divergence. Unhappily he was born into a period which was determined to see Paul as the Helleniser of Christianity and had not yet discovered the importance of eschatology. But Baur's grasp of the fact of divergence was the work of a mind eager for historical truth, even at the cost of misrepresentation and abuse, to which some present-day historians still find it necessary to contribute their quota.

To most British scholars it has appeared that the thesis of Baur and the Tubingen school had not merely been extravagantly stated but was fundamentally mistaken, if not perverse. Harnack and J. B. Lightfoot had exploded it. It could be regarded as an interesting cul-de-sac in the history of New Testament criticism, a brilliant but erratic *tour de force*. To those who are still of this mind it must be disconcerting that writers of world repute on Christian origins have found it less and less possible to take this view.

The most recent upholder of the orthodox position, Professor J. Munck, in his book entitled *Paulus und die Heilsgeschichte* (E. T. *Paul and the Salvation of Mankind*), laments that recognised authorities like W. L. Knox, Lietzmann, Nock, Dibelius, Goguel and Kümmel have been infected by Tubingen notions. Professor Munck is hard put to it to find ways of getting round the plain meaning of the evidence for a radical divergence between Paul and the Jerusalem church, not merely on policy but on fundamental interpretation of the Gospel. His book was trenchantly reviewed in the *Hibbert Journal*, July 1960, by G. S. F. Brandon, who concludes that "the Tubingen School showed that a real problem underlies Paul's role in the primitive Christian movement" and that it needs to be looked at afresh.

Marcion rejects Acts, as Tertullian informs us (De Scorp. 12) because it was untrue to the real story of Paul's relation to the original apostles as revealed in Galatians. It is ironical that this despised second-century heretic may now be credited with a truer historical and religious insight than his catholicising contemporaries. The Paul of history and of the genuine Epistles did not suit their need for one original, authoritative, apostolic tradition which would distinguish the true church from the heretics. It was necessary to believe that the teaching of the apostles in the beginning was identical and unalterable and its transmission divinely guaranteed. The process of rewriting history to meet the exigencies of the post-apostolic age is seen in Acts and the Pastorals, in Irenaeus and Tertullian. It leads to the Cyprianic doctrine of the one catholic church demonstrably distinguishable from the sects by all that came to be included in the notion of apostolicity.

Baur's history of the apostolic age has often been dismissed as written under the constraint of Hegelianism. But what he tried to explain was the fact that, in the most reliable testimony of the first age, he found at one point a radical difference of opinion between Paul and the rest of the apostles. In the later post-apostolic period the picture of the church and its mission involves a theory of unity which places all the apostles together at all points as the source of the one true and invariable doctrine.

Baur simply recognised and acknowledged the fact that the documents written by Paul openly and straightforwardly treat of this situation. A later age for dogmatic reasons prefers to ignore it. The theory of thesis, antithesis and synthesis is not read into the history but the history itself evinces these facts.

It is ludicrous to imagine Baur saying to himself: "Go to, I will make the first era of the church's existence exemplify the Hegelian theory of historical development." To discredit the theory is not to erase the history, as so many of Baur's critics have naïvely assumed. That can be attempted, in a fashion, only by preferring the account of Acts to the letters of Paul. This position Völter once attempted to maintain, in support of his contention that all the Pauline letters belong to the post-apostolic age. Today it is incredible.

The attacks on Paul's authority arose from the divergence as it showed itself in the question of the Law in relation to Gentile converts. It is safe to assume that no one would have questioned his right to teach, if his teaching had been in complete accord with the beliefs and practices of Jerusalem. An obvious way of countering deviation is to discredit the deviationist. This in Paul's case was not difficult since he was not one of the originals. In spite of his own conviction that he had seen the Lord, his seeing was not their seeing. If his apostleship were conceded it was open to others to make the same claim on the same subjective grounds.

Hence the importance then and later of the distinction between appearances and visions. Acts has accepted the orthodox view on this. If Paul saw the Lord, it was in some other fashion than that in which the apostles saw Him during his forty days with them which Acts records. Paul was not in the same sense a witness of the resurrection, though like all of them he could be a preacher of the resurrection.

The crux of the difference between Paul and the others was not the Law itself and how it ought to be regarded within the church, particularly by Gentile converts. It was the conception of the age in which Christians now live since the resurrection. The Jerusalem apostles waited for the coming of the new age, the restoration of the kingdom to Israel. The Law would then have fulfilled its God-appointed function. Till then it was as valid as ever and those who prepared for the new age were under its aegis. Thus it was to their minds obligatory for all who were being called into the company of the saints now awaiting the parousia.

Paul's inner certainty of the dramatic nature of God's intervention was such that he could live and speak as if there was no such interim. The belief that Christ had now been manifested through the resurrection, meant that the faith in this event created an entirely new situation in which the proclamation and acceptance of the Gospel had superseded everything else.

While the Jew might continue to live as he always had, as far as his bodily life was concerned, it was a denial of the efficacy of belief in the resurrection to require the believing Gentile to accept the Law as necessary to salvation. The new age is begun for the believer insofar as he believes; it is nothing to do with a relationship to the Law. This is true for the Jew as well as for the Gentile.

If this is the radical nature of the difference, we see how events helped to continue the stress that began with the distinctiveness of Paul's understanding of the Gospel as against that of the Jerusalem apostles. The delay of the parousia was a factor which told against Paul's view. But the increase of the Gentile church and the destruction of Jerusalem favoured the growth of Paul in the esteem of the church in general.

Though his theology could not be carried over as it was, and indeed was not transferable beyond the "last generation", namely his own, his name and his words when they were known became hallowed in the church of the empire. The task of catholic theology was to create out of the primitive situation a Christian theology which subsumed the qualities of the early church in such a way as to promote that unity of creed and organisation needed for the conditions of its own time.

CHAPTER ELEVEN

PAUL TODAY

AT the beginning of the century Heinrich Weinel began his book on the life and work of Paul as follows: "Paul once said of Moses, 'To this day a veil lies on their hearts when he is read' and at present the words may be applied to the apostle himself." He concluded his opening paragraph with the statement that "few, very few, really know him".

Sixty years have made no difference to the truth of his opening remark, but today not only would there be less certainty that there are even a few who know Paul, but a serious doubt whether it is even possible to "really know him". How has this change come about? What do we make of Paul today?

Since Weinel's day the attitude to history and the conception of what kind of history is possible have undergone profound change. Briefly, the notion that all you have to do is to get your facts and fit them up with the right interpretation is no longer tenable. The historian is aware today as never before that he is part of the history he writes. He sees his subject through his own eyes. Every new generation views past events from its own particular vantage point and there is no absolute point from which a full and final view is possible. There is no "impartial" or "ultimate" history which brings us face to face with "what really happened".

It sometimes seems as if historians are so conscious of this relative nature of their own station that they project it into the past also and speak as if the very past itself changes according to the viewer. Becker makes the statement that "the past is a kind of screen upon which each generation projects its vision of the future". This is true but not the whole truth.

Without taking up the question of the nature of history, it is still possible to recognise that when Weinel spoke of "really knowing" Paul he was taking a lot for granted which today is subject to question.

A change in our thinking about history is bound of course to affect our appreciation of the historical aspects of the Christian faith. This is most clearly seen in reference to the life of Jesus. There are no more lives of Jesus in the grand manner. Even if we are not disposed to follow Bultmann to the extreme scepticism which allows that all we can know of Jesus is that he lived, healed, preached and died at Roman hands, we have given up the idea that a biography of Jesus is possible.

Whether we go on to conclude that we ought therefore to give up the very search for what used to be the material of biography is another matter. In fact what is called the new quest for the historical Jesus is a negative answer to this question.

Apart from the philosophical query about whether we can ever "know" a historical person, there is doubt about whether we have the material for a biography of Paul. The day is past when it was sufficient to try to fit together material from Acts and Epistles to give a credible beginning, middle and end to Paul's life. The acids of historical criticism have burned away the framework. Matters which used to be regarded as the facts in the situation are no longer impregnable, for example the visits to Jerusalem and the three missionary journeys. More important, we recognise that our understanding of the mind of Paul is fluid.

But when all is said in this vein, there are still senses in which we can know about Paul and even know Paul, provided we are not overlooking the very valid points that historians make about the relativity of historical understanding. There is a real, worthwhile quest for the historical Paul and also a real knowledge of Paul. But in both cases the "facts" do not lie out there in the past waiting for us to uncover them so that they may impress us. Little is likely to be added to what we already have in the nature of information, but our understanding of Paul in history and Paul in experience can be enlarged and made our own in the twentieth century.

Consider how unacceptable Farrar's *Life of Christ* is today and in what respects it is inadequate. Though we do not attempt to write the life of Jesus, we know more than he did about it. We do not know many things he mistakenly thought he knew. There is a combination of knowledge and humility which forbids us to attempt what Farrar attempted. But at the same time this leaves no doubt that we know more of the historical Jesus than he did, though the "sum of facts" is less.

In the same way the biographies of Paul written half a century ago attempted to present a fuller and more comprehensive picture of Paul than present-day scholarship would afford. Yet the picture is less a picture of Paul than the fragmented knowledge of today can provide. It is unhistorical because it knows both more and less than there is to know.

This must mean that the task of historical criticism is never com-

plete. It is therefore naïve to speak as if there were an era of historical
criticism which New Testament scholars should be thankful to have
escaped in much the same way as they have escaped the Dark Ages,
merely in virtue of living in the mid-twentieth century.

If history is not simply the uncovering of latent facts but an
encounter with what is known, then there is no end to historical
criticism and each generation has to do its own in turn. Of course it
may happen that what was formerly thought to be known turns out
to be nothing more than a consensus of opinion which is now seen
to be based on false premises. Indeed the study of Paul during the
past 150 years is full of examples of this.

Historical criticism, therefore, is the process by which we come to
a better understanding of our subject through asking questions
which arise in our own day and through our own curiosity. The
relativity of history derives from the fact that each generation asks
its own questions which often cannot arise till the previous generation
has asked and answered the questions of its day.

In this way there is a knowing about Paul which is real, progressive
and worthwhile though never ultimate, and there will always be a
new quest for the historical Jesus and the historical Paul, even in
spite of the recognition that there can be no final knowledge. The
scepticism of a Bultmann is not a true historical but rather a philosophical scepticism which is not obligatory. We are never discharged
from the necessity to seek a historical understanding of the past.

But there is a sense in which knowing Paul is different from knowing about Paul. It may be that the Paul we speak of here is not the
Paul of historical research. But we need not enlarge on this at
present. What is meant by knowing Paul in this sense is something
different from becoming acquainted with the course of his life and
the way he coped with the conditions (not merely external) of his
own time. This kind of knowing tells us nothing about Paul who
lived and wrote in the first century, but something about the impression made on us by the Paul we think we meet in his letters and in
our own thoughts. More precisely, it is a knowing of ourselves
through what we think we know of Paul; more loosely, a meeting of
minds, although the other mind is our conception of the mind of Paul.

If those who approach Paul and his writings via existentialism are
telling us that this kind of meeting is possible and that it is not
dependent on a final historical knowledge of things which took place
in the first century, then they are so far right. This is akin to the
situation mentioned in a previous chapter regarding the use of the
twenty-third Psalm.

The letters of Paul can be used in this way and this may be called a knowledge of Paul, provided we are aware of what is happening. Here Paul is being used to meet the personal needs of those who believe they find in his letters what they most require; and it is to them according to their faith. How this Paul fulfils this function is a question which requires to take into account the fact that this Paul is endowed with a prestige in their eyes which generates faith. This prestige derives from the fame of the author, a fame which does not need to be specific and is not finally historical; from the fact that his letters are incorporated in the New Testament, by what process is immaterial; and from the status of the New Testament as the church's book. What the person, to whom Paul, the New Testament and the church are all numinous entities, recovers from the words of the apostle, is sacred to himself and may be the very breath of life to his inner man.

It is barely possible that this can be externalised so as to be the subject of discussion leading to the enlargement of our knowledge of the historical Paul. It is, after all, not theology or the knowledge of Paul as a theologian. It is an aspect of personal religion. The wayfaring-man in all of us is here (or elsewhere) finding food for his soul. He is not obliged to know its ingredients, still less to give an account of them, even if he could.

The theologian is apt to forget that it is by this kind of knowledge rather than by theology that the religious man lives. Theology is only what is said about that part of it which is capable of being expressed and discussed. But this Paul is the creation of the believer and need not be controlled by any desire or attempt of the believer to match him with the Paul so inaccessible to the historian. Doubtless, however, the believer is fully persuaded that the two are one.

Every great expositor of Paul has given us his attempt to reconcile the Paul he knows in this sense with the Paul he believes to have existed in the first century. Whether we think of Augustine or Luther, Wesley or Barth, the expositors give us the Paul of their heart married to the Paul of their mind, the two being one flesh as far as they are concerned.

But there is no finality in this process, nor can there be. It is not ridiculous for a modern theologian to give us his version of what Luther, with the help of Augustine, understood to be the mind of Paul, unless he thinks he is the end of a long line of faithful trustees who guarantee the delivery of an original precious deposit. Unhappily this is too often what theologians do think, in spite of the fact that time is very cruel to theological tomes.

Most theologians are not burdened by a sense of the relativity of theology. Philosophers and historians may find themselves in a world in which they themselves are no longer Olympian observers of the flux of things but immersed in the dynamics of existence. Theological treatises, however, are apt to begin from an assumption of static objectivity which leads them to the view that their function is to expound a final unvarying deposit of truth given in a kerygma which is the same yesterday, today and forever, though the idiom of its expression may change from generation to generation.

Since the Pauline Epistles are basic to the kerygma, the exposition of these Epistles is thought to be a method of transmitting the kerygma. The theology of Paul is therefore to be carried over into every succeeding age. Even if there are matters in the letters that are not transferable, this is supposed not to affect the original deposit, only the earthen vessel in which it is contained.

The demythologising controversy has sharply pointed up the impossibility of merely lifting the theology of Paul out of the first century into the twentieth. At the same time it has raised several crucial questions for theology itself. Paul's world is not ours, if in fact it is anyone else's but Paul's. It is not merely that the cosmology of the first century is impossible for us today, though many theologians write as if this were so and the theology of Paul simply requires to be set in a new frame. The possibility of treating the Epistles as if they afforded a core of central truth enfolded in a wrapper which might be discarded and replaced by something more congenial to our time, is open only to those who will not see how radical the problem is.

The processes by which a world peopled by demons and heading for catastrophic eclipse is made significant today, are generally artificial. The attempt, for example, to revivify and translate to our own time the sense of imminent disaster present in the Epistles by stressing the possibility of nuclear destruction in the twentieth century, is an exercise in ingenuity. To say that the eschatological beliefs of the early church are still important, because they now mean the world is going somewhere and is not purposeless, this is substitution not interpretation.

If it is no longer possible to believe in the second coming of Christ, the honourable thing is to say so and to recognise that such a belief belongs to a past age. There is no obligation to perpetuate its existence by ingenious and ingenuous methods, any more than it is necessary or possible to perpetuate the medicine of the ancient world by "re-interpreting" the notion of demon possession as embryonic virology.

We account for certain illnesses today in ways that have no relation to the prognosis and diagnosis of the first century, and feel no need to maintain that nevertheless the truth about these illnesses and their treatment is incapsulated in the medicine of the ancient world. But the theologian feels that he must maintain that the truth about the nature and destiny of modern man is somehow to be distilled from the letters of Paul, after suitable disjunction of the temporary from the eternal, the husk from the core, and re-interpretation of the latter.

There was a Paul who was a man of his age, so it seems; but there is also another Paul whose words are oracles for all time. It is the theologian's business to decipher what the oracle is saying today. What the man of his age said can be discarded, so long as the deposit of truth and its transmission are both guaranteed. But Paul's world was a unity to him and his theology belongs to it.

This crude analysis of the treatment of Paul's theology within the church is not a travesty. The true believer in the twentieth century has still not shaken off the fascination of verbal inspiration. He cherishes the desire to find that his own gropings after enlightenment are seconded by the authority of a Christian Apollo. The psychological need for such an oracular figure is no guarantee that he does or could exist.

Christians have traditionally felt obliged to make their own experience conform to that of the apostle as they understood it, and to use his terminology even when the attempt was seen to be futile. Paul's experience has generally been regarded as normative. The likelihood is that Paul's experience and his interpretation of it were his own, and neither in content nor in expression capable of being a pattern for the ordinary Christian. Insofar as its expression was dominated by his conception of the Christian life as the life of a new age lived in conditions of the old, it was applicable only to those who shared the presumption that any day the old would pass away and the new come into being.

When the parousia was postponed to the end of the world in the thinking of post-apostolic ages, this kind of context for Christian living was gone. The continued use of the phraseology belonging to it became conventional. The psychology and cosmology remained, but the theology was no longer spontaneous and the meaning of Christ, his death and resurrection, the sacraments and the sanctions of the Christian life could no longer be Paul's, even if his terminology continued to be used.

The Paulinism of Augustine, Luther and their more recent successors is not a transcript of Paul but a vivifying of their own understanding of aspects of Paul's thought in their own experience, whether of natural depravity, justification by faith, conversion or the otherness and grace of God. In no case is it a continuation or a revival of the theology of Paul. It is their own theology read back into their study of his Epistles, a study induced by generations of traditional teaching that from there the truth of the Gospel was to break forth. Only the existentialist seems to be aware of the nature of his indebtedness to the letters of Paul. But even he will often speak as if the "word" is in Paul and not in himself.

There are two forthright intentions in reading Paul's letters. One is with a view to the historical understanding of the kind of man he was and the kind of thoughts that animated him. Any such study results in a knowledge of the conditions of the early church and the uniqueness of the apostle in endowments and achievement.

To ask what is the good of this, as if the only thing that mattered were immediate experience, is to call in question the validity of all historical study. Life is not only an immediate "now". It is enlarged and enriched by its emplacement in its own past and future. Even its "now" is not a self-generated, unrelated instant of experience. It is what it is in virtue of its congruity with what is known and hoped for. Historical theology is not mere antiquarianism any more than the study of history itself is merely an interesting hobby. The knowledge of great minds enriches, even if it is never possible to import what we have come to know as a substantive bloc into our experience. The theology of Paul remains the theology of Paul, however accurate our apprehension of it and even if we are mistaken enough to try to duplicate it in ourselves. It is not life but food.

The second forthright intention in reading Paul is the frank use of the letters as inspirational and devotional material. We have already remarked on this as the most widespread service given by the literature, uninhibited as it is by intellectual queries or the curiosity to "really know" Paul.

The intellectual freedom implied in such a use of the material is vital to its profitability. The emphasis is not on knowing but on finding food for the soul's present need. This of course does not involve the conclusion that it can be found here only, although in all probability the numinous element in such a quest, and the con- servatism of the intellectually destitute ensure that it will be found here more readily and more acceptably than elsewhere.

It is an unhappy heritage that insists that the primary factor in regard to the letters of Paul is their theology and that the doctrine of Paul is somehow obligatory in every age for those who would call themselves Christian. They are right who argue that the life of Paul is more than his teaching, if by this they mean that an understanding of how he grappled with the questions of human destiny in thought and deed in his own age is of more consequence than the theoretical knowledge of his answers to the problems of his own day and his own mind.

Theology has recently moved from the emphasis on credal propositions to talking of the essence of the Gospel as inherent in events, "the mighty acts of God". This seems to be a new recognition of the importance of the historical element. But it comes at a time when the historicity of events is most difficult to establish. Is there a halfway house between reliance on the historical in the New Testament as it was conceived in Western civilisation up to our own times, and the thesis that history has nothing to contribute to the existential truth of the Gospel and all that is needed is the proclamation of the kerygma which brings men face to face with God here and now?

This depends largely on whether God acts in the world in a miraculous fashion or not and, if He does, whether this is detectable. Most theologians who speak of the mighty acts of God seem to think the answer is "yes" in both cases. For some the detection is a matter which historical investigation can cope with, while for others it is faith alone that "observes" God at work.

The importance of Paul in such circumstances is that he declares the kerygma, the mighty acts of God, as facts of history. God sent from heaven His Son who inaugurated His kingdom by supernatural actions, was crucified, rose from the grave, re-ascended to heaven and will return to judge the living and the dead. The belief which theologians regard as constituting Christian faith is at least the belief that this is a true statement of what happened or will happen in history, and that this is the core of Paul's teaching, the permanently valid element, the Gospel.

But if today, as is the case, it is possible for masses of people, including some theologians, to believe that this schema is mythological, and that what is known of Jesus historically is something other than this, the question immediately arises as to how the declarations of Paul, can have more than historical interest, except where historical knowledge is a matter of indifference. Does God meet men irrespective of whether any of the "mighty acts" really happened? or irrespective of whether they can be detected? or irrespective of history?

Overbeck once said that, "Nowadays no one has understood Paul if he thinks he can still agree with him. The opponents of this assertion involuntarily confirm it by the way they distort his words in order to wrest from them a satisfactory meaning."

TABLES

TABLE 1

Sentence Length Distribution—THE EPISTLE OF JAMES

No. of words in Sentence	Number of sentences in Epistle			
	f	x	fx	fx^2
1— 5	34	−2	−68	136
6—10	54	−1	−54	54
11—15	36		−122	
16—20	22	+1	22	22
21—25	7	+2	14	28
26—30	1	+3	3	9
31—35	2	+4	8	32
55	1	+8	8	64
	157		+55	345

Constant	Value	Standard Error
Mean	10·9	0·6
Median	9·1	0·6
First Quartile	5·5	0·5
Third Quartile	14·1	0·8
Ninth Decile	18·9	0·9

TABLE 2

Sentence Length Distributions—THE EPISTLES OF CLEMENT

No. of Words in Sentence	No. of Sentences in I CLEMENT						No. of Sentences in II CLEMENT			I and II CLEMENT
	Sample 1	2	3	4	Remainder	Total	Sample 1	Remainder	Total	Total
1—5	26	26	32	27	11	122	21	9	30	152
6—10	42	45	42	43	20	192	41	16	57	249
11—15	34	42	41	33	22	172	43	15	58	230
16—20	13	13	19	22	12	79	18	11	29	108
21—25	16	9	8	8	14	55	14	8	22	77
26—30	6	5	4	8	4	27	7	4	11	38
31—35	5	5	1	5	4	20	6	3	9	29
36—40	3	3	—	1	4	11	—	—	—	11
41—45	—	2	1	1	3	7	—	—	—	7
46—50	2	—	—	—	—	2	—	—	—	2
51—55	1	—	—	—	—	1	—	2	2	3
56—60	2	—	1	1	1	5	—	—	—	5
61—65	—	—	1	1	1	4	—	—	—	4
66—70	—	—	—	—	1	1	—	—	—	1
71—75	—	—	—	—	1	1	—	—	—	1
76—80	—	—	—	—	1	1	—	—	—	1
81—85	—	—	—	—	1	1	—	—	—	1
No. of Sentences	150	150	150	150	99	699	150	68	218	917
No. of Words	2,187	1,942	1,815	2,005	1,851	9,800	1,975	1,033	3,008	12,808

TABLE 2 (Contd.)

Sentence Length Distributions—THE EPISTLES OF CLEMENT

I CLEMENT

Sample	Mean	Standard Error	Median	Standard Error	First Quartile	Standard Error	Third Quartile	Standard Error	Ninth Decile	Standard Error
1	14·6	0·9	11·0	0·9	6·4	0·6	19·0	2·0	28·3	3·1
2	12·9	0·8	10·5	0·7	6·4	0·6	14·9	0·6	25·0	3·7
3	12·0	0·7	10·1	0·7	5·6	0·6	14·7	0·6	20·6	4·6
4	13·3	0·8	10·8	0·9	6·2	0·6	17·2	1·2	26·3	2·3
Total	15·0	0·4	11·0	0·4	6·4	0·3	17·4	0·7	26·7	1·5

II CLEMENT

Sample	Mean	Standard Error	Median	Standard Error	First Quartile	Standard Error	Third Quartile	Standard Error	Ninth Decile	Standard Error
1	13·3	0·6	11·5	0·7	7·0	0·6	17·1	1·5	24·3	2·6
Total	13·9	0·6	11·9	0·6	7·1	0·6	18·2	1·1	23·8	1·0
Grand Total	14·0	0·07	11·3	0·33	6·6	0·26	17·6	0·6	26·5	1·2

TABLE 3

Sentence Length Distributions—CLEMENT OF ALEXANDRIA

No. of Words in Sentence	Rich Man's Salvation	Exhortation to the Greeks	No. of Words in Sentence	Rich Man's Salvation	Exhortation to the Greeks
1—5	36	20	51—55	3	4
6—10	37	38	56—60	3	1
11—15	24	41	61—65	2	1
16—20	27	32	66—70	1	—
21—25	16	21	71—75	2	1
26—30	12	15	76—80	1	—
31—35	14	9	81—85	—	—
36—40	4	7	101—105	1	—
41—45	8	8	111—115	1	—
46—50	8	2	No. of Sentences	200	200

1. RICH MAN'S SALVATION
2. EXHORTATION TO THE GREEKS

	Mean	Standard Error	Median	Standard Error	First Quartile	Standard Error	Third Quartile	Standard Error	Ninth Decile	Standard Error
1	21·2	1·4	15·6	1·3	6·9	0·8	29·2	2·5	46·3	2·7
2	18·9	0·9	15·2	1·1	7·6	0·8	24·5	1·5	37·9	3·0

TABLE 4

Sentence Length Distributions—HERODOTUS

No. of Sentences in Book

No. of Words in Sentence	1	2	3	4	5	6	7	8	9
1—5	16	6	7	8	13	8	10	9	13
6—10	35	33	48	38	47	30	36	42	45
11—15	47	34	37	49	43	35	46	43	54
16—20	39	39	34	38	32	41	38	33	28
21—25	24	26	21	24	26	29	23	27	23
26—30	16	22	23	15	14	30	19	18	14
31—35	11	19	6	15	9	10	10	10	6
36—40	5	5	11	8	2	3	4	9	9
41—45	4	4	6	2	5	6	4	4	4
46—50	1	6	2	—	4	5	5	3	—
51—55	1	1	3	1	2	1	3	1	2
56—60	—	—	2	—	—	—	2	—	1
61—65	—	—	—	1	2	1	—	—	—
66—70	—	1	—	—	—	—	—	—	—
71—75	—	1	—	—	1	1	—	1	1
76—80	—	2	—	—	—	—	—	—	—
81—85	—	1	—	—	1	—	—	—	—
86—90	—	1	—	1	—	—	—	—	—
101—105	—	—	—	—	—	—	—	—	—
No. of Sentences	200	200	200	200	200	200	200	200	200

Mean Sentence Length—19·184 words

TABLE 4 (Contd.)

Sentence Length Distributions—HERODOTUS

Book	Mean	Standard Error	Median	Standard Error	First Quartile	Standard Error	Third Quartile	Standard Error	Ninth Decile	Standard Error
1	17·8	0·5	15·3	0·9	8·4	0·9	22·7	1·3	31·4	1·9
2	22·0	1·0	18·5	0·9	11·6	0·9	27·7	1·4	36·0	4·2
3	19·4	0·8	16·2	1·0	9·5	0·6	25·7	1·3	36·8	1·9
4	18·9	0·9	15·7	0·9	10·4	0·6	23·5	1·3	32·7	1·4
5	17·7	0·8	14·7	0·8	8·9	0·7	22·9	1·2	32·8	2·4
6	20·5	0·8	18·3	0·9	11·7	0·9	26·2	1·0	33·5	2·1
7	19·2	0·8	16·1	0·9	10·4	0·7	22·2	1·3	34·0	2·1
8	18·8	0·8	15·9	1·1	9·9	0·7	22·4	1·1	34·0	2·1
9	17·4	0·8	13·9	0·7	9·1	0·7	22·2	1·3	32·5	3·5

TABLE 5

Sentence Length Distributions—THUCYDIDES

No. of Words in Sentence	No. of Sentences in Book							
	1	2	3	4	5	6	7	8
1—5	5	5	5	4	5	6	6	12
6—10	28	32	32	20	29	17	24	19
11—15	36	36	37	38	31	29	31	36
16—20	25	34	34	34	35	36	31	28
21—25	32	25	25	27	27	34	31	31
26—30	17	17	16	21	20	18	23	12
31—35	12	14	18	24	12	23	15	17
36—40	12	5	12	10	10	4	10	10
41—45	9	8	11	9	8	5	7	13
46—50	10	9	2	3	6	4	6	5
51—55	6	5	4	1	6	4	3	3
56—60	—	—	—	4	2	5	3	1
61—65	3	3	1	1	1	5	4	3
66—70	4	2	2	1	1	2	1	4
71—75	—	1	1	1	1	2	2	1
76—80	—	—	—	1	1	—	—	2
81—85	—	1	—	—	1	1	1	1
86—90	—	—	—	—	—	1	—	—
91—95	—	1	—	—	1	1	2	1
96—100	—	—	—	—	—	—	—	1
101—105	—	—	—	—	—	2	—	—
106—110	—	—	—	—	—	—	—	—
111—115	—	1	—	—	—	—	—	—
116—120	1	—	—	—	1	—	—	—
121—125	—	—	—	—	—	1	—	—
126—130	—	—	—	—	1	—	—	—
155—160	—	—	—	—	—	—	—	—
No. of Sentences	200	200	200	200	200	200	200	200

Mean Sentence Length—25·016 words

TABLE 5 (Contd.)

Sentence Length Distributions—*THUCYDIDES*

Work	Mean	Standard Error	Median	Standard Error	First Quartile	Standard Error	Third Quartile	Standard Error	Ninth Decile	Standard Error
1	24·9	1·2	20·9	1·1	12·4	0·9	32·9	2·5	47·0	2·1
2	24·4	1·3	19·0	1·0	11·8	0·9	30·4	2·2	46·1	2·4
3	22·5	1·0	18·8	1·0	11·8	0·8	30·3	1·7	40·5	1·9
4	24·2	1·0	20·7	1·3	13·4	0·8	31·3	1·3	39·9	2·1
5	24·8	1·4	20·0	1·0	12·6	1·0	31·3	2·5	47·5	3·5
6	27·5	1·3	21·8	1·0	14·7	1·1	32·2	1·3	55·0	5·3
7	25·3	1·2	21·3	1·1	13·2	1·0	31·3	2·0	46·7	3·5
8	25·4	1·3	20·8	1·1	12·6	0·9	33·5	1·8	47·0	4·2

TABLE 6

Sentence Length Distributions—PHILO JUDAEUS

No. of Sentences in Works

No. of Words in Sentence	On the Creation	Sacrifice of Cain & Abel	Cherubim	Worse Attacks the Better	Posterity of Cain	Giants
1—5	7	9	12	9	16	12
6—10	27	34	29	34	30	25
11—15	42	46	27	45	39	28
16—20	33	27	32	27	40	29
21—25	21	19	26	19	25	14
26—30	21	20	14	20	20	18
31—35	12	9	14	10	13	8
36—40	14	13	11	13	6	3
41—45	13	4	7	4	8	5
46—50	2	7	9	7	—	3
51—55	4	1	6	1	—	5
56—60	1	4	2	4	1	—
61—65	2	—	3	—	—	1
66—70	—	4	2	4	1	2
71—75	—	—	2	—	—	—
76—80	—	—	1	—	—	—
81—85	—	1	—	1	1	—
86—90	—	—	—	—	—	—
91—95	—	1	—	1	1	—
96—100	—	1	1	1	1	2
101—105	1	—	—	—	—	—
116—120	—	—	1	—	—	—
121—125	1	—	1	—	—	—
146—150	—	—	1	—	—	—
No. of Sentences	200	200	200	200	200	154

TABLE 6 (Contd.)

Sentence Length Distributions—PHILO JUDAEUS
Allegorical Interpretation of Genesis

No. of Words in Sentence	Sample 1	Sample 2	Sample 3	Total
1—5	22	20	25	67
6—10	47	44	47	138
11—15	37	46	27	110
16—20	38	38	41	117
21—25	22	24	16	62
26—30	17	9	13	39
31—35	7	9	11	27
36—40	5	5	2	12
41—45	3	3	11	17
46—50	1	–	–	1
51—55	–	–	1	1
56—60	–	–	2	2
61—65	–	–	1	1
66—70	–	1	1	2
71—75	1	1	–	2
76—80	–	–	2	2
No. of Sentences	200	200	200	600

TABLE 6 (Contd.)

Sentence Length Distributions—PHILO JUDAEUS

1 ON THE CREATION
2 SACRIFICE OF CAIN & ABEL
3 CHERUBIM
4 WORSE ATTACKS THE BETTER
5 POSTERITY OF CAIN
6 GIANTS

Work	Mean	Standard Error	Median	Standard Error	First Quartile	Standard Error	Third Quartile	Standard Error	Ninth Decile	Standard Error
1	22·7	1·0	18·6	1·1	11·9	0·7	29·8	1·5	41·2	1·6
2	22·6	1·2	17·0	1·3	10·8	0·7	28·7	1·5	43·7	5·5
3	25·8	1·5	20·0	1·1	11·7	1·1	33·6	2·2	49·4	2·4
4	22·4	1·2	17·2	1·4	10·8	0·7	29·0	1·5	43·7	5·5
5	21·6	0·9	17·1	0·9	10·6	0·8	25·0	1·2	38·5	3·5
6	20·2	0·9	17·1	1·1	10·3	1·0	27·1	1·5	41·6	2·3

TABLE 6 (Contd.)

Sentence Length Distributions—*PHILO JUDAEUS*

Allegorical Interpretation of Genesis

Sample	Mean	Standard Error	Median	Standard Error	First Quartile	Standard Error	Third Quartile	Standard Error	Ninth Decile	Standard Error
1	16·3	0·7	14·2	0·9	8·0	0·7	21·4	1·4	29·1	1·2
2	16·3	0·7	13·9	0·9	8·4	0·7	20·4	1·3	29·9	2·4
3	18·2	1·0	15·1	0·9	7·7	0·7	23·1	1·9	35·0	1·9
Total	16·9	0·5	14·3	0·6	8·0	0·4	21·5	0·9	31·3	1·4

TABLE 7

Sentence Length Distributions—DIODORUS SICULUS

No. of Words in Sentence	Book 1		Book 2	Book 21	Book 22	Book 32	Total
	Sample 1	Sample 2					
1—5	3	—	—	3	7	2	15
6—10	4	8	9	10	22	29	82
11—15	28	25	39	46	43	35	216
16—20	50	39	57	30	35	43	254
21—25	31	32	39	31	18	38	189
26—30	25	36	20	14	9	16	120
31—35	23	22	16	7	11	15	94
36—40	14	12	10	8	8	8	60
41—45	8	8	3	2	1	1	23
46—50	1	6	4	1	2	4	18
51—55	4	5	1	3	—	2	15
56—60	—	5	—	1	—	1	7
61—65	3	—	—	1	—	—	3
66—70	1	—	—	—	—	1	3
71—75	2	—	—	—	—	—	2
76—80	—	—	—	—	—	—	—
81—85	2	1	1	1	—	—	3
86—90	—	—	—	—	—	—	1
91—95	—	—	—	—	—	—	1
96—100	1	—	1	—	—	—	1
101—105	—	—	—	—	—	—	1
106—110	—	1	1	—	—	—	2
No. of Sentences	200	200	200	158	156	195	1,109

TABLE 7 (Contd.)

Sentence Length Distributions—*DIODORUS SICULUS*

Book	Mean	Standard Error	Median	Standard Error	First Quartile	Standard Error	Third Quartile	Standard Error	Ninth Decile	Standard Error
1—1	26·4	1·0	22·4	1·1	16·5	0·6	32·0	1·3	41·3	3·8
1—2	25·4	1·0	24·4	1·1	17·2	0·8	32·3	1·4	43·8	3·8
2	22·7	0·9	18·7	1·2	16·0	0·5	29·0	1·5	35·8	1·9
21	21·3	1·0	18·3	1·1	12·9	0·6	24·8	0·9	35·8	1·6
22	23·0	0·8	15·9	0·8	11·2	0·8	22·3	1·5	32·0	1·1
32	20·8	0·8	19·0	1·2	17·2	0·7	26·0	1·9	38·1	3·8

TABLE 8

Sentence Length Distributions—LYSIAS

No. of Sentences in Work

No. of Words in Sentence	1	2	3	6	7	12	13	14	19	20
1—5	10	1	4	12	2	15	11	3	7	4
6—10	21	19	10	20	15	35	46	14	39	35
11—15	30	20	20	36	23	48	40	16	26	23
16—20	18	13	20	30	16	28	33	14	27	12
21—25	15	18	14	14	10	22	24	16	32	20
26—30	13	17	10	6	10	13	16	11	10	7
31—35	6	12	5	6	8	10	10	3	9	5
36—40	6	12	5	12	1	11	7	5	4	3
41—45	2	12	3	1	5	6	7	5	5	1
46—50	1	4	3	2	2	5	2	6	2	—
51—55	1	—	2	—	3	2	1	2	1	1
56—60	2	2	1	1	—	3	1	1	1	1
61—65	1	—	—	1	—	—	1	—	1	1
66—70	—	1	—	—	—	1	—	—	—	—
71—75	—	4	—	—	—	1	1	—	—	—
76—80	—	1	1	—	—	—	—	1	—	—
90—95	—	—	—	—	—	—	—	1	—	—
96—100	—	1	—	—	—	—	—	—	—	—
101—105	—	2	—	—	—	—	—	—	—	—
121—125	—	1	—	—	—	—	—	—	—	—
No. of Sentences	126	140	98	141	95	200	200	98	164	112

TABLE 8 (Contd.)

Sentence Length Distributions—LYSIAS

Work	Mean	Standard Error	Median	Standard Error	First Quartile	Standard Error	Third Quartile	Standard Error	Ninth Decile	Standard Error
1	19·2	1·2	15·6	1·6	10·1	0·8	25·2	1·9	35·3	2·8
2	29·2	1·7	24·7	1·6	13·8	1·3	37·1	2·1	47·5	4·4
3	22·3	1·0	18·5	1·2	12·6	1·0	27·8	2·1	40·3	5·0
6	18·5	1·0	15·4	1·0	10·5	0·7	22·8	1·8	36·2	1·5
7	21·0	1·2	17·3	1·5	12·0	0·9	27·6	2·1	41·5	2·9
12	20·0	1·0	15·4	1·3	10·0	0·9	25·8	2·4	39·1	1·8
13	18·8	0·9	15·5	1·1	9·2	0·7	24·2	1·2	35·0	2·1
14	23·1	1·6	20·6	1·5	12·3	1·3	29·8	1·9	48·0	7·4
19	19·0	0·9	16·9	1·2	9·4	0·7	28·8	2·8	33·7	2·1
20	17·2	1·0	13·7	1·2	8·4	0·7	22·5	1·2	29·9	3·2

TABLE 9

Sentence Length Distribution—DEMOSTHENES

No. of Words in Sentence	No. of Sentences in Work											
	3	4	6	7	8	9	10	13	14	15	18	19
1—5	20	29	17	6	26	28	14	9	15	3	31	28
6—10	25	19	19	12	35	40	38	10	19	12	29	42
11—15	27	29	17	18	30	35	39	24	21	21	36	33
16—20	25	30	14	14	30	35	21	15	20	19	25	26
21—25	16	10	7	14	15	20	18	9	20	16	19	11
26—30	7	6	7	11	21	17	21	12	7	11	16	14
31—35	3	9	5	10	13	10	16	7	7	12	10	13
36—40	6	7	2	8	10	7	4	4	6	3	7	9
41—45	2	4	2	3	7	3	11	2	2	3	4	4
46—50	2	2	2	1	4	4	4	3	5	2	6	4
51—55	—	4	4	—	1	4	1	1	1	2	5	3
56—60	1	4	—	1	1	5	3	1	1	1	4	3
61—65	—	1	—	—	—	1	3	2	1	—	2	3
66—70	1	1	—	—	1	2	1	1	—	1	1	2
71—75	—	2	2	1	3	2	4	2	—	—	2	1
76—80	1	1	1	—	1	1	1	1	1	—	1	—
81—85	1	1	—	—	1	—	—	1	—	—	1	1
86—90	—	—	1	1	1	—	—	—	1	—	—	—
91—95	—	—	—	—	—	2	—	—	—	—	—	1
96—100	—	—	—	—	—	—	—	—	—	—	1	—
101—105	—	—	—	1	—	—	—	—	1	—	—	1
106—110	—	—	—	—	—	—	—	—	—	—	1	—
111—115	—	—	—	1	—	—	—	—	—	—	1	—
151—155	—	—	—	—	—	—	—	—	—	—	—	—
No. of Sentences	136	159	100	101	200	212	199	102	127	103	200	200

TABLE 9 (Contd.)

Sentence Length Distributions—DEMOSTHENES

No. of Words in Sentence	No. of Sentences in Work												
	20	21	22	23	24	25	27	29	30	32	34	35	37
1—5	20	19	34	44	36	28	13	23	7	14	8	14	42
6—10	29	29	24	36	34	29	33	37	16	13	27	32	38
11—15	38	31	34	41	28	38	30	28	10	23	35	24	47
16—20	29	31	31	19	18	31	40	26	12	18	28	14	27
21—25	26	26	32	23	20	24	29	21	15	6	21	19	33
26—30	22	14	17	13	9	12	20	23	15	6	12	12	13
31—35	11	11	12	5	4	7	15	7	6	3	9	5	6
36—40	9	12	7	4	7	7	5	7	7	6	5	8	6
41—45	7	8	4	4	1	9	9	8	3	3	3	6	4
46—50	1	4	2	3	3	4	5	5	4	3	2	—	1
51—55	2	5	—	5	2	3	—	2	—	2	1	2	3
56—60	—	—	1	2	—	4	2	—	1	—	1	2	1
61—65	1	4	—	—	1	1	1	2	2	1	1	1	—
66—70	1	—	—	1	1	—	2	—	2	1	1	—	—
71—75	—	1	—	—	1	1	2	2	1	—	1	—	—
76—80	2	1	2	—	1	1	—	—	—	—	—	1	—
81—85	1	1	—	—	1	1	—	—	—	—	1	—	—
86—90	1	1	—	—	—	—	—	—	—	—	1	1	1
91—95	—	—	—	—	2	—	—	—	—	—	—	—	1
106—110	—	1	—	—	—	—	—	—	—	—	—	1	—
111—115	—	1	—	—	—	—	1	1	—	—	—	—	—
116—120	—	—	—	—	—	—	—	—	—	—	—	—	—
No. of Sentences	200	200	200	200	170	200	207	192	100	99	157	142	223

TABLE 9 (Contd.)

Sentence Length Distributions—DEMOSTHENES

No. of Words in Sentence	No. of Sentences in Work											
	38	39	40	41	43	44	45	47	48	49	50	55
1—5	11	25	5	9	27	12	23	6	8	7	5	5
6—10	21	30	13	15	29	25	28	31	25	15	24	19
11—15	15	36	13	23	31	47	39	41	15	24	29	26
16—20	18	24	19	10	26	44	41	24	28	18	20	17
21—25	13	12	14	10	21	22	21	18	21	25	16	17
26—30	5	17	15	15	12	21	13	27	14	11	18	6
31—35	5	7	17	3	16	10	12	15	11	10	15	9
36—40	5	4	9	5	7	10	11	11	9	12	6	1
41—45	2	3	3	3	10	4	5	2	6	10	8	3
46—50	2	2	8	1	4	3	—	4	4	8	7	1
51—55	1	1	4	2	6	—	3	4	3	2	3	1
56—60	—	1	3	1	2	1	3	3	1	1	2	—
61—65	—	1	1	1	1	—	1	2	—	4	1	2
66—70	—	—	2	—	5	—	—	1	1	—	1	—
71—75	—	—	2	—	1	1	1	3	1	3	2	—
76—80	—	—	—	—	2	—	—	3	1	—	2	—
81—85	—	—	2	—	—	1	1	1	—	—	2	—
86—90	—	—	1	—	—	—	—	—	—	—	1	—
91—95	—	—	—	—	—	—	—	2	—	—	—	—
101—105	—	—	—	—	—	—	1	—	—	—	2	—
106—110	1	—	—	—	—	—	—	—	1	—	—	—
116—120	—	—	—	—	—	—	—	—	—	1	1	—
130—135	—	—	1	—	—	—	—	—	—	—	1	—
156—160	—	—	—	—	—	—	—	1	—	—	—	—
No. of Sentences	99	163	132	98	200	200	200	200	149	152	165	108

TABLE 9 (Contd.)

Sentence Length Distributions—DEMOSTHENES

No. of Words in Sentence	No. of Sentences in Work					
	56	57	58	59	60	61
1—5	8	25	23	7	3	5
6—10	28	31	36	23	11	18
11—15	21	37	30	24	27	23
16—20	25	32	22	27	16	23
21—25	16	26	21	22	18	26
26—30	12	20	11	16	15	20
31—35	12	9	17	21	9	11
36—40	1	8	13	11	6	6
41—45	2	5	5	12	1	3
46—50	3	2	4	5	4	5
51—55	4	3	2	6	4	2
56—60	—	—	3	4	—	2
61—65	2	2	3	7	—	—
66—70	1	—	—	3	—	2
71—75	1	—	4	2	—	—
76—80	2	—	4	—	—	2
81—85	2	—	—	2	—	—
86—90	—	—	2	1	—	—
91—95	—	—	—	—	—	—
96—100	—	—	—	1	—	—
101—105	—	—	—	2	—	—
106—110	1	—	—	1	—	—
126—130	—	—	—	—	—	—
131—135	—	—	—	1	—	1
141—145	—	—	—	1	—	—
156—160	—	—	—	1	—	—
No. of Sentences	141	200	200	200	114	149

TABLE 9 (Contd.)

Sentence Length Distributions—DEMOSTHENES

Work	Mean	Standard Error	Median	Standard Error	First Quartile	Standard Error	Third Quartile	Standard Error	Ninth Decile	Standard Error
3	17·2	1·1	14·3	1·1	7·8	1·0	21·6	1·6	34·0	5·9
4	19·9	1·4	15·4	1·1	7·8	1·4	21·9	2·7	40·3	4·7
6	20·0	1·8	15·1	1·8	7·1	1·1	25·7	3·1	45·0	7·5
7	23·8	1·8	20·2	1·8	12·0	1·2	30·4	2·2	38·6	1·9
8	20·6	1·1	16·5	1·2	8·4	0·9	28·3	1·5	40·0	2·1
9	19·8	1·1	15·4	1·0	8·1	0·8	25·2	1·8	44·7	7·3
10	22·3	1·1	17·0	1·7	9·7	0·8	29·6	1·5	43·7	1·8
13	22·7	1·8	19·3	1·7	11·9	0·9	33·6	3·1	44·5	7·5
14	20·5	1·3	17·1	1·4	9·4	1·3	25·2	3·6	39·4	2·8
15	21·4	1·1	18·7	1·3	12·6	1·1	27·8	2·0	34·5	1·3
18	21·7	1·4	15·8	1·4	8·3	1·1	25·0	1·6	37·9	3·0
19	21·0	1·3	14·6	1·3	7·5	0·7	28·6	2·2	45·0	5·3
20	20·7	1·1	17·2	1·2	10·1	0·8	30·0	1·3	37·7	2·3
21	23·0	1·3	18·4	1·1	10·3	1·0	24·2	2·2	44·4	2·6
22	18·3	0·9	16·3	1·1	8·3	1·3	22·2	1·0	33·3	1·8
23	16·4	1·2	12·4	0·9	5·8	0·9	25·0	1·3	34·0	4·2
24	18·6	1·1	14·4	1·0	7·1	0·9	25·0	1·7	36·3	5·3
25	20·2	1·1	15·7	1·2	8·8	1·0	27·6	2·6	37·8	2·3
27	21·5	1·1	18·4	0·9	11·0	1·0	27·0	1·6	40·7	2·4
29	20·3	1·1	16·5	1·3	8·4	0·8	30·0	1·3	40·5	2·6
30	23·7	1·5	21·7	2·5	11·0	2·2	25·2	1·4	43·3	5·0
32	19·2	1·4	14·8	1·1	7·6	1·7	24·7	3·6	41·7	5·0
34	22·7	1·1	16·5	1·1	10·6	0·8	26·5	1·3	36·3	3·8

TABLE 9 (Contd.)

Sentence Length Distributions—DEMOSTHENES

Work	Mean	Standard Error	Median	Standard Error	First Quartile	Standard Error	Third Quartile	Standard Error	Ninth Decile	Standard Error
35	20·6	1·4	15·4	2·1	8·3	0·8	22·0	2·2	39·9	2·2
37	16·5	0·9	13·4	0·8	6·8	0·9	21·9	1·0	30·6	3·7
38	17·9	1·3	14·2	1·7	7·7	1·0	20·7	1·7	40·0	7·5
39	16·9	0·9	13·7	0·9	7·6	0·9	22·6	2·3	31·9	2·7
40	29·6	1·7	25·7	1·9	15·5	1·3	36·7	1·5	53·5	4·3
41	20·1	1·4	16·0	2·2	10·1	0·9	27·2	1·4	38·2	3·0
43	23·3	1·4	17·5	1·4	9·3	1·1	31·3	1·9	46·3	5·3
44	19·5	0·8	16·8	0·8	11·4	0·7	22·7	1·4	29·8	1·0
45	19·3	0·9	16·2	0·9	9·8	0·8	24·3	1·5	36·4	1·8
47	25·7	1·5	19·6	1·5	11·6	0·7	28·7	1·1	38·6	1·8
48	23·5	1·3	19·7	1·1	11·4	1·8	30·4	2·4	42·6	3·1
49	26·4	1·4	22·6	1·2	13·4	1·1	37·3	2·2	49·1	2·3
50	27·7	1·7	21·4	2·0	12·1	1·0	40·5	3·5	81·3	2·8
55	19·6	1·1	16·2	1·5	10·6	0·9	24·1	1·3	34·0	1·7
56	22·8	1·6	17·7	1·2	9·9	0·9	28·2	2·2	47·2	5·9
57	18·7	0·9	16·1	1·1	9·0	1·0	24·8	1·2	35·0	2·4
58	22·9	1·3	19·7	1·6	10·2	1·0	32·1	1·8	47·5	5·3
59	31·3	1·8	24·3	1·6	14·2	1·3	39·6	2·8	61·4	3·0
60	22·9	1·1	20·0	1·6	14·5	0·9	33·1	2·6	38·0	2·7
61	24·6	1·6	21·0	1·2	13·1	1·2	31·7	2·1	48·5	3·7

TABLE 10

Sentence Length Distributions—ISOCRATES

No. of Words in Sentence	No. of Sentences in Work											
	1	2	3	4	5	6	7	8	9	10	11	12
1—5	6	—	2	7	8	2	5	7	6	3	4	11
6—10	58	15	17	13	26	14	18	17	13	13	7	19
11—15	60	36	34	30	32	25	35	24	25	17	11	23
16—20	38	28	29	27	33	42	38	30	40	17	16	16
21—25	12	22	23	17	30	40	16	31	25	18	22	27
26—30	6	16	17	29	18	19	16	24	17	22	16	19
31—35	7	3	12	13	12	15	13	15	6	9	3	18
36—40	3	4	8	8	9	11	10	10	6	9	6	14
41—45	2	3	3	13	1	7	12	16	8	6	3	10
46—50	—	4	5	9	7	3	4	4	7	6	7	6
51—55	—	2	2	7	4	3	5	6	5	1	3	7
56—60	1	1	1	4	4	8	1	5	5	—	3	7
61—65	—	2	—	5	1	—	3	4	4	3	—	1
66—70	—	—	—	4	3	2	4	1	1	—	1	2
71—75	—	—	2	—	1	2	1	2	—	1	—	1
76—80	—	—	—	2	3	1	1	1	1	—	1	4
81—85	—	—	1	1	2	2	—	—	—	2	—	1
86—90	—	—	—	—	2	—	—	1	1	—	—	2
91—95	—	1	—	2	—	1	—	—	—	1	—	3
96—100	—	—	—	1	2	—	—	—	1	—	—	3
101—105	—	—	—	2	—	1	—	—	—	—	—	—
106—110	—	—	—	—	2	—	—	—	—	—	—	2
111—115	—	—	—	2	—	1	—	—	—	—	—	—
116—120	—	—	—	—	—	1	—	—	—	—	—	1
121—125	—	—	—	1	—	—	—	1	1	—	—	1
126—130	—	—	1	—	—	—	—	1	—	—	—	—
131—135	—	—	—	—	—	1	—	—	—	—	—	—
136—140	—	—	—	1	—	—	—	—	—	—	—	1
146—150	—	—	—	—	—	—	—	—	—	1	—	—
156—160	—	—	—	—	—	—	—	—	—	1	—	1
186—190	—	—	—	1	—	—	—	—	—	—	—	—
No. of Sentences	193	137	157	200	200	200	182	200	172	130	103	200

L

TABLE 10 (Contd.)

Sentence Length Distributions—ISOCRATES

No. of Words in Sentence	No. of Sentences in Work								
	13	14	15	16	17	18	19	20	21
1—5	—	3	5	2	11	3	5	1	1
6—10	4	17	20	13	19	24	21	3	13
11—15	2	16	20	12	29	30	16	7	13
16—20	9	18	31	10	28	30	26	6	12
21—25	7	21	37	13	15	19	24	10	10
26—30	5	12	22	14	13	14	11	5	2
31—35	2	8	15	13	10	11	4	5	—
36—40	3	10	16	4	13	8	6	4	4
41—45	3	5	8	2	3	4	4	1	1
46—50	2	5	9	4	3	3	4	1	—
51—55	2	—	5	3	2	4	3	1	1
56—60	—	3	5	3	2	1	2	—	—
61—65	—	4	—	—	—	—	1	1	1
66—70	—	1	2	1	1	—	—	—	1
71—75	1	—	1	1	—	1	—	1	—
76—80	—	1	—	—	1	1	—	—	—
81—85	—	—	1	1	—	—	—	—	—
86—90	1	—	—	—	—	1	—	—	—
91—95	—	—	1	2	—	1	—	—	—
96—100	1	—	1	—	—	—	—	1	1
101—105	—	—	—	—	—	1	1	—	—
106—110	1	—	—	1	—	—	1	—	—
111—115	—	—	1	—	—	—	—	1	—
116—120	—	—	—	1	—	—	—	—	—
121—125	—	—	—	—	—	—	—	—	—
No. of Sentences	42	124	200	99	152	155	128	46	58

TABLE 10 (Contd.)

Sentence Length Distributions—ISOCRATES

Work	Mean	Standard Error	Median	Standard Error	First Quartile	Standard Error	Third Quartile	Standard Error	Ninth Decile	Standard Error
1	14·9	0·6	12·7	0·6	6·8	0·5	18·7	0·8	24·9	1·7
2	22·3	1·1	18·0	1·0	12·7	0·8	25·6	1·8	39·1	4·4
3	23·7	1·3	19·4	1·1	12·8	0·8	28·8	1·5	39·6	2·4
4	29·5	2·3	26·0	1·2	15·0	1·0	42·3	2·4	63·0	4·2
5	30·0	1·3	20·2	1·2	12·5	1·0	31·3	2·5	44·6	21·2
6	28·0	1·3	22·1	0·9	16·1	0·7	32·8	1·9	53·3	7·1
7	25·1	1·2	19·9	0·9	13·2	0·8	33·3	2·2	46·0	5·1
8	28·2	1·3	23·5	1·1	15·3	1·0	36·0	3·1	52·0	3·5
9	26·7	1·5	20·4	1·3	14·8	1·2	32·5	5·0	51·8	3·9
10	28·6	2·0	24·2	1·6	12·5	1·4	34·2	2·7	47·5	2·9
11	26·5	1·5	23·1	1·2	16·2	1·3	32·1	7·1	48·4	2·2
12	33·8	2·0	26·1	1·9	14·4	1·3	41·5	3·1	70·0	10·6
14	25·5	1·4	21·9	1·3	13·4	1·5	33·8	3·0	46·6	3·4
15	27·9	1·3	23·2	1·0	15·8	1·0	35·0	2·0	48·3	2·4
16	29·1	2·1	24·8	1·9	14·4	1·8	36·6	5·4	70·0	15·0
17	22·6	1·1	18·0	1·1	11·4	0·9	29·6	2·1	39·8	1·4
18	23·0	1·3	18·4	1·0	11·9	0·9	28·7	1·9	40·6	4·6
19	22·0	1·2	19·2	1·1	11·9	1·5	26·8	2·2	41·5	4·3

TABLE 11

Sentence Length Distributions—PLATO

No. of Words in Sentence	EPISTLE SEVEN	APOLOGY	No. of Words in Sentence	EPISTLE SEVEN	APOLOGY
1—5	17	68	66—70	3	1
6—10	41	103	71—75	4	2
11—15	51	95	76—80	–	–
16—20	44	61	81—85	6	–
21—25	36	48	86—90	3	–
26—30	34	39	91—95	–	–
31—35	25	20	96—100	1	–
36—40	20	15	101—105	–	2
41—45	12	8	116—120	1	–
46—50	10	7	121—125	–	1
51—55	8	4	151—155	1	–
56—60	5	4	No. of Sentences	326	483
61—65	4	5			

TABLE 11 (Contd.)

Sentence Length Distributions—PLATO

EPISTLE SEVEN

Mean	Standard Error	Median	Standard Error	First Quartile	Standard Error	Third Quartile	Standard Error	Ninth Decile	Standard Error
26·7	1·2	21·4	1·3	12·3	0·8	34·3	1·6	52·1	3·4

APOLOGY

17·1	0·6	13·7	0·6	7·6	0·5	23·7	1·0	35·6	2·2

TABLE 12

THE COMMON WORDS OF THE NEW TESTAMENT

Total number of words in the New Testament=137,328

Word	No. of Occurrences	Proportion of Occurrences
"Ho", "He", "To"	19,734	14·4
"Kai"	8,947	6·5
"Autos"	5,534	4·0
"De"	2,771	2·0
"En"	2,713	2·0
"Einai"	2,450	1·8
Total for all six words	42,149	30·4 per cent.

These figures are from Morgenthaler, *Statistik des Neutestament-lichen Wortschatzes*, Zurich, 1958, and refer to Nestle's Text 21st Edition.

TABLE 13

The Occurrence of "Kai" in Twenty-Word Samples of the Epistle to the Galatians

No. of "Kais" in Each Sample	Number of Such Samples in the Epistle	
	Expected	Observed
0	57·9	62
1	37·6	32
2	12·3	12
3 or more	3·1	5

TABLE 14

The Spacing of "Kai" in the Epistle to the Galatians

Size of Space between Successive "Kais", in words	Number of Spaces	
	Expected	Observed
1—10	19·7	25
11—20	14·2	14
21—30	10·3	8
31—40	7·5	11
over 40	19·3	13
Totals	71·0	71

TABLE 15

The Occurrence of "Kai" in the History of Thucydides

Sample	Occurrence of "Kai"	Number of Words in Sample
1·1	96	1,370
1·2	69	1,165
1·3	66	1,266
1·4	87	1,209
2·1	79	1,242
2·2	78	1,201
2·3	97	1,202
2·4	74	1,232
3·1	81	1,092
3·2	66	1,123
3·3	76	1,168
3·4	58	1,111
4·1	81	1,155
4·2	89	1,310
4·3	76	1,278
4·4	68	1,126
5·1	98	1,276
5·2	92	1,352
5·3	105	1,409
5·4	119	1,426
6·1	81	1,185
6·2	107	1,369
6·3	98	1,158
6·4	74	1,245
7·1	74	1,080
7·2	91	1,295
7·3	105	1,371
7·4	96	1,313
8·1	109	1,566
8·2	98	1,165
8·3	95	1,163
8·4	91	1,228
	2,774	39,851

Chi Squared $= 14·0$

Degrees of Freedom $= 31$

TABLE 16

The Occurrence of "Kai" in the History of Herodotus

Sample Number	Occurrence of "Kai"	Number of Words in Sample
1	31	946
2	27	772
3	37	935
4	38	903
5	46	1,111
6	54	1,355
7	40	1,130
8	43	910
9	33	973
10	38	1,045
11	37	916
12	29	953
13	34	834
14	37	1,035
15	43	990
16	34	962
17	32	719
18	40	944
19	41	887
20	42	1,065
21	28	964
22	46	1,109
23	39	1,023
24	42	982
25	47	1,074
26	39	844
27	26	820
28	42	1,102
29	36	1,037
30	38	972
31	25	871
32	44	870
33	32	1,042
34	21	795
35	26	755
36	45	907
	1,332	34,552

TABLE 17

The Occurrence of "Kai" in the Works of Plato

Work	Occurrence of "Kai"	Total	Proportion of "Kai"
LAWS			
1–200	180	3,353	0·0540
201–400	185	3,489	0·0530
APOLOGY			
1–200	161	3,087	0·0522
201–400	197	4,100	0·0480
PHAEDO			
	156	2,944	0·0530
CRITO			
1–200	143	2,673	0·0535
THEAETETUS			
	119	2,071	0·0580
	1,141	21,717	0·0525
AXIOCHUS	137	2,349	0·0583
EPISTLE SEVEN	473	8,798	0·0540

TABLE 18

The Occurrence of "Kai" in the Works of Clement of Alexandria

1. Rich Man's Salvation
2. Exhortation to The Greeks
3. To the Newly Baptised

	Work	Occurrence of "Kai"	Total	Proportion of "Kai"
1	1—50	77	1,055	0·073
	51—100	88	1,189	0·074
	101—150	80	986	0·081
	151—200	102	1,013	0·101
		347	4,243	0·082
2	1—50	64	1,048	0·061
	51—100	62	976	0·063
	101—150	57	959	0·059
	151—200	41	785	0·052
		224	3,768	0·059
3		56	668	0·083
	Total for all samples	627	8,679	0·072

TABLE 19

The Occurrence of "Kai" in THE EPISTLES OF CLEMENT

Epistle	Occurrence of "Kai"	Total	Proportion of "Kai"
I CLEMENT			
1	183	2,187	0·0840
2	127	1,942	0·0654
3	107	1,815	0·0590
4	123	2,005	0·0614
Remainder	139	1,851	0·0751
Total	679	9,800	0·0685
II CLEMENT			
1	113	1,975	0·0572
Remainder	65	1,033	0·0630
Total	178	3,008	0·0592
GRAND TOTAL for I & II CLEMENT	857	12,808	0·0670

TABLE 20

The Occurrence of "Kai" in the Books of DIODORUS SICULUS

Book	Occurrence of "Kai"	Total	Proportion of "Kai"
1			
1—200	267	5,287	0·0505
201—400	276	5,368	0·0514
2	212	4,536	0·0467
21			
1—158	140	3,348	0·0420
22			
1—156	168	2,871	0·0590
32			
1—195	189	4,060	0·0470
Total	1,252	25,470	0·0491

TABLE 21

The Occurrence of "Kai" in the Works of LYSIAS

Work	Occurrence of "Kai"	Number of Words in Work	Proportion of "Kai"
1	101	2,414	0·0420
2	179	4,078	0·0440
3	107	2,182	0·0490
4	46	952	0·0483
5	9	279	0·0333
6	145	2,637	0·0550
7	86	2,030	0·0424
8	34	1,039	0·0330
9	21	879	0·0240
10	52	1,493	0·0350
11	14	550	0·0255
12	174	3,979	0·0440
13	195	3,754	0·0520
14	106	2,429	0·0440
15	22	604	0·0364
16	40	1,146	0·0350
17	25	584	0·0430
18	68	1,352	0·0503
19	151	3,124	0·0483
20	77	1,915	0·0402
21	63	1,294	0·0490
22	30	1,128	0·0270
23	26	774	0·0340
24	51	1,433	0·0360
25	63	2,022	0·0312
26	58	1,388	0·0420
27	26	752	0·0332
28	57	914	0·0624
29	29	664	0·0440
30	79	1,886	0·0420
31	48	1,819	0·0264
32	84	1,704	0·0493
33	20	432	0·0463
34	22	559	0·0394
35	40	1,087	0·0370
Totals of Works 1—35	2,348	55,222	

TABLE 22

The Occurrence of "Kai" in the Works of LYSIAS:

No. of "Kais" in Sentence	Number of Sentences								
	1	3	6	12	13	14	19	25	30
No "Kai"	64	41	64	102	80	51	70	47	44
One	35	29	45	57	76	20	52	21	26
Two	19	16	15	25	24	14	30	8	14
Three	6	5	7	9	12	3	9	4	3
Four	—	4	5	3	6	5	3	2	—
Five	2	3	3	1	1	3	—	—	2
Six	—	—	1	1	1	1	—	1	1
Seven	—	—	—	—	—	—	—	—	—
Eight	—	—	1	1	—	1	—	—	—
Nine	—	—	—	1	—	—	—	—	—
No. of Sentences in Sample	126	98	141	200	200	98	164	83	90
Chi Squared	0·1	1·8	3·4	1·1	8·8	2·4	6·4	2·1	1·1
Degrees of Freedom	3	4	4	4	4	3	4	3	3

TABLE 23

The Occurrence of "Kai" in Sentences—LYSIAS
The Data Fitted to a Negative Binomial Distribution

Sentences having:	Observed	Expected
No "Kai"	500	504·9
One	314	314·2
Two	150	145·4
Three	53	59·4
Four	22	22·8
Five	12	
Six	5 ⎤	
Seven	– ⎥	12·6
Eight	1 ⎥	
Nine	1 ⎦	
	1,058	1,059·3

Chi Squared $= 4·2$

Degrees of Freedom $= 3$

TABLE 24

The Occurrence of "Kai" in Sentences in the Works of ISOCRATES—A

No. of "Kais" in Sentence	Number of Sentences in Works										
	1	2	3	4	5	6	7	8	9	10	11
No "Kai"	140	59	51	72	81	92	76	77	55	57	36
One	41	39	53	48	63	47	42	51	57	30	38
Two	8	26	27	40	25	38	29	31	28	19	16
Three	4	8	14	18	11	11	18	23	11	11	7
Four	—	2	7	9	11	5	7	11	12	8	4
Five	—	1	2	5	3	3	5	3	5	3	—
Six	—	2	2	3	2	3	2	1	1	1	2
Seven	—	—	2	3	1	—	2	3	1	1	—
Eight	—	—	—	1	1	—	1	—	—	—	—
Nine	—	—	—	—	2	—	—	—	1	—	—
Ten	—	—	—	—	—	—	—	—	1	1	—
Eleven	—	—	—	—	—	1	—	—	—	—	—
Nineteen	—	—	—	1	—	—	—	—	—	—	—
No. of Sentences	193	137	158	200	200	200	182	200	172	131	103
Chi Squared	78·8	5·0	6·5	8·1	4·4	5·4	2·1	4·2	9·8	1·5	6·4
Degrees of Freedom	2	3	4	4	4	4	4	4	4	4	3

TABLE 24 (Contd.)

The Occurrence of "Kai" in Sentences in the Works of ISOCRATES—A

No. of "Kais" in Sentence	Number of Sentences in Work							
	12	14	15	16	17	18	19
No "Kai"	76	54	82	41	71	76	53
One	43	45	57	24	43	51	40
Two	33	10	26	15	15	15	15
Three	11	8	21	10	16	8	11
Four	13	3	5	3	5	5	5
Five	12	4	5	–	2	–	1
Six	4	–	4	2	–	–	3
Seven	2	–	–	2	–	–	–
Eight	4	–	–	–	–	–	–
Nine	2	–	–	–	–	–	–
Eleven	–	–	–	1	–	–	–
No. of Sentences	200	124	200	98	152	155	128
Chi Squared	33·4	8·4	4·6	0·5	6·1	11·5	1·6
Degrees of Freedom	4	3	4	3	3	3	3

M

TABLE 24 (Contd.)

The Occurrence of "*Kai*" in the Works of ISOCRATES—B

Work	Occurrence of "Kai"	No. of Words in Work
1	69	2,903
2	140	3,006
3	213	3,737
4	311	6,539
5	250	5,352
6	220	5,600
7	249	4,572
8	270	5,635
9	250	4,601
10	171	3,721
11	119	2,748
12	342	6,750
13	60	1,322
14	121	3,182
15	241	5,499
16	133	2,872
17	151	3,369
18	125	3,562
19	146	2,923
20	44	1,120
21	46	1,095
Totals for Works 2—21	3,602	77,205
Epistle		
1	15	585
2	59	1,278
3	20	420
4	48	824
5	10	281
6	47	888
7	46	780
8	37	664
9	62	1,134
Total for Epistles 1—9	344	6,854

TABLE 24 (Contd.)

The Occurrence of "Kai" in Sentences—ISOCRATES—C

The Data Fitted to a Negative Binomial Distribution

Sentences having	Observed	Expected	Sentences having	Observed	Expected
No "Kai"	1,034	1061·1	Six	28	26·4
One	727	685·3	Seven	15	13·2
Two	373	382·5	Eight and Over	11	12·2
Three	208	202·4	Total	2,540	2539·7
Four	102	104·1			
Five	42	52·5			

Chi Squared = 6·2   Degrees of Freedom = 6

TABLE 25

The Occurrence of "Kai" in the Works of DEMOSTHENES

Work	Occurrence of "Kai"	Number of Words in Work	Proportion of "Kai"
1	97	1,835	0·0529
2	105	2,045	0·0513
3	107	2,358	0·0454
4	178	3,283	0·0542
5	88	1,457	0·0604
6	126	1,995	0·0632
7	109	2,422	0·0450
8	254	4,232	0·0600
9	257	4,192	0·0613
10	243	4,414	0·0550
11	63	1,288	0·0490
12	45	1,414	0·0320
13	135	2,320	0·0581
14	105	2,582	0·0410
15	74	2,200	0·0340
16	79	1,857	0·0425
17	76	1,790	0·0425
18	292	4,346	0·0672
19	251	4,171	0·0601
20	146	4,117	0·0354
21	245	4,656	0·0530
22	121	3,641	0·0332
23	125	3,289	0·0380
24	135	3,702	0·0364
25	255	4,047	0·0630
26	85	1,686	0·0501
27	231	4,567	0·0505
28	70	1,510	0·0440
29	157	3,899	0·0402
30	113	2,351	0·0480
31	37	950	0·0390

TABLE 25 (Contd.)

The Occurrence of "Kai" in the Works of DEMOSTHENES

Work	Occurrence of "Kai"	Number of Words in Work	Proportion of "Kai"
32	88	1,909	0·0460
33	96	2,544	0·0380
34	132	3,256	0·0405
35	157	2,908	0·0540
36	198	3,947	0·0501
37	190	3,577	0·0531
38	101	1,846	0·0580
39	86	2,740	0·0313
40	187	3,906	0·0480
41	77	1,957	0·0393
42	117	2,231	0·0524
43	204	4,261	0·0480
44	152	3,887	0·0391
45	138	3,822	0·0361
46	60	1,558	0·0385
47	291	5,374	0·0541
48	242	3,512	0·0690
49	187	4,358	0·0430
50	263	4,609	0·0570
51	56	1,344	0·0420
52	109	2,115	0·0515
53	102	2,009	0·0510
54	223	3,180	0·0701
55	92	2,112	0·0440
56	137	3,248	0·0422
57	211	3,622	0·0580
58	203	4,673	0·0434
59	454	6,268	0·0724
60	118	3,259	0·0362
61	157	3,670	0·0430

TABLE 26

The Occurrence of "Kai" in Small Samples—DEMOSTHENES—A

No. of Occurrences of "Kai"	Work 1	2	3	4	6	7	8	9	10	13	14	15	18
No "Kai"	34	35	46	53	26	52	65	47	46	37	61	59	46
One	29	38	43	58	38	36	76	51	61	43	41	34	55
Two	21	18	20	33	20	27	43	33	30	21	20	11	32
Three	3	9	5	10	13	5	19	15	7	11	3	6	12
Four	3	1	2	5	2	1	5	4	4	2	4	–	3
Five	1	1	–	1	–	–	3	–	2	2	–	–	2
Six	–	–	–	–	–	–	–	–	–	–	–	–	–
No. of Samples	91	102	118	160	99	121	211	150	150	116	129	110	150
No. of "Kai"	97	110	108	179	125	109	254	178	168	136	106	74	177
Mean	1·06	·67	·92	1·12	1·26	·90	1·20	1·19	1·12	1·17	·82	·67	1·18
Variance	1·13	·74	·88	1·17	1·10	·88	1·27	1·13	1·14	1·28	·97	·75	1·20

No. of Occurrences of "Kai"	19	20	21	22	23	24	25	27	29	30	33	34	35
No "Kai"	35	75	46	76	67	70	48	47	61	48	50	65	47
One	57	52	53	52	57	55	48	57	58	39	60	57	52
Two	43	19	36	20	20	18	27	36	25	20	15	22	32
Three	14	3	13	2	6	6	20	8	4	7	2	5	11
Four	1	–	2	–	–	1	6	2	2	2	–	1	2
Five	–	–	–	–	–	–	1	–	–	1	–	–	–
No. of Samples	150	150	150	150	150	150	150	150	150	117	127	150	144
No. of "Kai"	189	99	172	98	115	113	191	161	128	113	96	120	157
Mean	1·26	·66	1·05	·65	·77	·75	1·27	1·07	·85	·75	·75	·80	·90
Variance	·88	·60	1·01	·57	·69	·75	1·43	·89	·78	1·11	·57	·73	·97

The Occurrence of "Kai" in Small Samples—DEMOSTHENES—A (Contd.)

No. of Occurrences of "Kai"	Work 36	37	39	40	42	43	44	45	47	48	49	50	52
No "Kai"	59	40	73	56	38	59	59	69	51	36	52	43	35
One	50	72	51	51	44	54	61	58	55	52	63	49	39
Two	33	28	8	34	20	25	24	21	37	38	26	36	24
Three	6	10	5	7	11	10	6	2	6	17	8	18	6
Four	1	—	1	2	—	—	—	—	1	7	1	3	1
Five	1	—	—	—	—	1	—	—	—	—	—	1	—
Six	—	—	—	—	—	—	—	—	—	—	—	—	—
No. of Samples	150	150	138	150	113	150	150	150	150	150	150	150	105
No. of "Kai"	144	158	86	148	117	145	127	106	152	207	143	192	109
Mean	·95	1·05	·62	·99	1·04	·97	·85	·71	1·01	1·38	·95	1·28	1·04
Variance	·94	·72	·66	·91	·91	1·10	·69	·57	·81	1·23	·79	1·21	·92

No. of Occurrences of "Kai"	53	54	55	56	57	58	59	60	61
No "Kai"	38	32	43	58	37	62	26	58	57
One	33	58	39	67	64	52	58	38	64
Two	18	41	19	21	33	27	40	16	21
Three	11	12	3	4	14	9	20	13	6
Four	—	5	1	—	2	—	5	2	1
Five	—	2	—	—	—	—	1	—	1
No. of Samples	100	150	105	150	150	150	150	127	150
No. of "Kai"	102	121	90	121	180	133	223	117	133
Mean	1·02	·81	·86	·81	1·33	·89	1·49	·92	·89
Variance	1·00	·55	·77	·55	1·16	·82	1·14	1·12	·84

The Occurrence of "Kai" in Small Samples—DEMOSTHENES—B

Total For Twenty-Four Accepted Works

	Observed	Poisson Expectation		Observed	Poisson Expectation
No "Kai"	1,376	1,375	Three	200	205
One	1,313	1,321	Four	47	47
Two	644	636	Five	11	11

Mean—0·959   Variance—1·048

TABLE 27

The Occurrence of "Kai" in Sentences in the History of HERODOTUS

Number of Occurrences of "Kai" in Sentence	Number of Sentences in Book									Total
	1	2	3	4	5	6	7	8	9	
0	107	91	108	98	110	97	105	106	113	935
1	66	68	63	74	53	66	58	63	62	573
2	16	18	16	18	22	26	24	21	18	179
3	9	16	11	6	8	8	8	9	4	79
4	–	5	1	2	5	2	3	–	2	20
5	2	1	1	1	1	1	2	–	–	9
										–
7	–	1	–	1	1	–	–	–	1	4
12								1		1
Number of Sentences in Sample	200	200	200	200	200	200	200	200	200	1,800

mean rate of occurrence 0·74 "Kai" per sentence.

Chi Squared = 26·5

Degrees of Freedom = 24

TABLE 28

The Occurrence of "Kai" in Sentences in the History of THUCYDIDES—A

No. of Occurrences of "Kai"	Number of Sentences in Sample from Books								Total
	1	2	3	4	5	6	7	8	
No "Kai"	48	50	50	41	28	45	41	34	337
One	70	70	81	69	65	68	60	60	543
Two	48	31	36	61	52	42	46	49	365
Three	11	25	15	12	27	15	26	29	160
Four	10	12	10	6	10	15	15	11	89
Five	8	6	5	6	9	7	4	9	54
Six	3	2	3	2	4	6	4	4	28
Seven	1	2	—	3	1	1	2	2	12
Eight	—	1	—	—	—	1	—	—	2
Nine	—	1	—	—	—	—	2	1	4
Ten	1	—	—	—	—	—	—	—	1
Eleven	—	—	—	—	2	—	—	—	2
Twelve	—	—	—	—	1	—	—	1	2
Fourteen	—	—	—	—	1	—	—	—	1
No. of Sentences in Sample	200	200	200	200	200	200	200	200	1,600

Mean = 1·962 "Kai" per Sentence   Variance = 3·418 "Kai" per Sentence

	1	2	3	4	5	6	7	8	Total
Chi Squared	4·4	6·8	6·9	10·1	9·3	4·2	5·0	6·6	53·3
Degrees of Freedom	6	6	6	6	6	6	6	6	42

B

Variation	Sum of Squares	Degrees of Freedom	Quotient
Between Samples	1951·6	7	278·8
Within Samples	43420·7	75	579·2

Variance Ratio = 2·08 $n_1 = 7$ $n_2 = 75$ Not significant

TABLE 29

The Occurrence of Sentences which have "De" as the Second or Third Word

HERODOTUS

Book	Sentences having "De" as Second or Third Word	No. of Sentences in Sample
1	91	200
2	89	200
3	101	200
4	97	200
5	98	200
6	98	200
7	70	200
8	92	200
9	92	200

Chi Squared = 13·4 for 8 Degrees of Freedom

THUCYDIDES

Book	Sentences having "De" as Second or Third Word	No. of Sentences in Sample
1	95	200
2	95	200
3	90	200
4	90	200
5	97	200
6	81	200
7	85	200
8	82	200

Chi Squared = 5·5 for 7 Degrees of Freedom

TABLE 30

The Occurrence of "De" in LYSIAS

Work	Sentences Beginning with "De"	Sentences in the Work
1	43	126
2	49	140
3	38	98
6	44	141
12	73	200
13	81	200
14	34	98
19	51	164
25	24	83
30	30	90

Chi Squared $= 7.0$

Degrees of Freedom $= 8$

TABLE 31

The Occurrence of "De" at the Start of Sentences in the Works of

DEMOSTHENES

Work	No. of Sentences Beginning with "De"	No. of Sentences in Work	Work	No. of Sentences Beginning with "De"	No. of Sentences in Work
1	18	91	32	28	100
2	23	90	33	40	118
3	26	136	34	48	158
4	37	159	35	41	142
5	13	54	36	36	202
6	9	100	37	59	223
7	33	101	38	23	99
8	39	200	39	35	163
9	51	212	40	46	132
10	34	199	41	24	98
11	11	47	42	23	110
12	17	65	43	63	200
13	36	102	44	59	200
14	29	127	45	67	200
15	26	103	46	18	73
16	25	84	47	80	205
17	20	76	48	49	153
18	43	200	49	50	155
19	40	200	50	64	168
20	35	200	51	13	68
21	40	200	52	27	87
22	45	200	53	32	74
23	42	200	54	41	143
24	39	200	55	24	109
25	46	200	56	37	143
26	18	73	57	47	200
27	66	207	58	39	203
28	18	83	59	73	200
29	44	192	60	23	114
30	22	100	61	35	149
31	4	51			
	949	4,252		1,244	4,389

TABLE 32

The Occurrence of "De" at the Start of Sentences in Two Works of
CLEMENT OF ALEXANDRIA

Work	No. of Sentences with "De" as Word 2 or 3	No. of Sentences in Sample
RICH MAN'S SALVATION	41	200
EXHORTATION TO THE GREEKS	53	200

Chi Squared = 2·1 for 1 Degree of Freedom

TABLE 33

The Occurrence of "De" at the Start of Sentences in the Works of
ISOCRATES

Work	Sentences beginning with "De"	No. of sentences in Work
1	31	196
2	21	137
3	35	158
4	54	200
5	63	200
6	73	200
7	43	182
8	67	200
9	48	172
10	46	131
11	28	103
12	47	200
14	36	124
15	64	200
16	36	98
17	53	152
18	65	155
19	39	128
Total (Work 1 excluded)	818	2,740

TABLE 34

The Occurrence of "De" at the Start of Sentences in Some Works of PLUTARCH

Work	No. of Sentences with "De" as Word 2 or 3	Proportion	No. of sentences Sample
OLD MEN IN PUBLIC AFFAIRS	64	0·32	200
PRECEPTS OF STATECRAFT	61	0·305	200
LIFE OF THESEUS	110	0·55	200
LIFE OF ROMULUS	101	0·505	200
LIVES OF THE TEN ORATORS	124	0·62	200

TABLE 35

The Occurrence of "De" at the Start of Sentences in Some Works of JOSEPHUS

Work	No. of Sentences with "De" as Word 2 or 3	No. of Sentences in Sample
ANTIQUITIES		
Book 1	104	200
2	96	200
3	105	200
4	94	200
JEWISH WAR		
Book 4	86	200
5	101	200
6	77	200
7	93	200
LIFE SENTENCES		
1—200	97	200
201—400	81	200

TABLE 36

The Occurrence of "De" in the Second Position in the Works of HERODOTUS

No. of Occurrence of "De"	Works 1	2	3	4	5	6	7	8	9	Total
No "De"	163	144	148	130	147	141	157	158	159	1,347
One	31	42	47	57	41	51	36	36	35	376
Two	6	10	3	7	10	8	6	5	6	61
Three	–	4	2	4	2	–	–	–	–	12
Four	–	–	–	1	–	–	–	–	–	1
Five	–	–	–	1	–	–	1	–	–	2
Six	–	–	–	–	–	–	–	–	–	–
Seven	–	–	–	–	–	–	–	1	–	1
No. of Sentences in Sample	200	200	200	200	200	200	200	200	200	1,800

Chi Squared = 30.9   Degrees of Freedom = 16

TABLE 37

The Occurrence of "De" in the Second Position in the Works of THUCYDIDES

No. of Occurrences of "De"	Works 1	2	3	4	5	6	7	8	Total
No "De"	154	163	157	148	149	156	162	163	1,252
One	33	32	38	45	37	36	29	32	282
Two	13	5	5	7	14	8	9	5	66
No. of Sentences in Sample	200	200	200	200	200	200	200	200	1,600

Chi Squared = 17·3

Degrees of Freedom = 14

TABLE 38

The Occurrence of "De" in the Second Position in the Works of ISOCRATES

No. of Occurrences of "De"	Works 1	2	3	4	5	6	7	8	9	10	11	12	13	14	15	16	17	18	19
No "De"	138	95	123	125	140	132	123	129	116	80	65	134	27	85	134	58	117	109	99
One	51	35	27	41	39	44	45	49	38	37	29	48	11	28	48	26	26	37	18
Two	4	6	4	16	11	11	8	16	10	6	5	10	2	9	14	4	6	5	9
Three	1	2	3	11	5	9	4	4	5	4	3	4	1	2	2	4	3	4	1
Four	2	–	–	4	1	2	1	–	2	2	–	3	–	–	2	3	–	–	1
Five	–	–	1	1	4	1	1	–	–	1	1	1	1	–	–	3	–	–	–
Six	–	–	–	2	–	1	–	2	–	1	–	–	–	–	–	–	–	–	–
Ten	–	–	–	–	–	–	–	–	1	–	–	–	–	–	–	–	–	–	–
No. of Sentences in Sample	196	138	158	200	200	200	182	200	172	131	103	200	42	124	200	98	152	155	128

N

TABLE 39

The Occurrence of "En" in the History of HERODOTUS

No. of Occurrences of "En"	Books 1	2	3	4	5	6	7	8	9	Total
No "En"	164	172	170	170	176	166	174	170	157	1,519
One	31	21	23	27	23	29	23	23	40	240
Two	4	6	7	3	1	5	3	7	3	39
Three	1	1	–	–	–	–	–	–	–	2
No. of Sentences in Sample	200	200	200	200	200	200	200	200	200	1,800

Chi Squared = 10·0   Degrees of Freedom = 8

TABLE 40

The Occurrence of "En" in the History of THUCYDIDES

No. of Occurrences of "En"	Books								Total
	1	2	3	4	5	6	7	8	
No "En"	155	143	164	138	159	160	148	149	1,216
One	40	42	28	46	36	27	40	44	303
Two	5	11	7	12	2	9	10	4	60
Three	–	4	1	2	1	2	2	2	14
Four	–	–	–	2	2	1	–	1	6
Five	–	–	–	–	–	1	–	–	1
No. of Sentences in Sample	200	200	200	200	200	200	200	200	1,600
	0·3	1·0	3·3	5·7	0·6	1·1	0·4	1·5	

Chi Squared = 26·5   Degrees of Freedom = 14

TABLE 41

The Occurrence of "En" in the Works of ISOCRATES

No. of Occurrences of "En"	Work																			Total
	1	2	3	4	5	6	7	8	9	10	11	12	13	14	15	16	17	18	19	
No "En"	176	125	133	167	176	167	152	170	142	115	94	165	37	114	174	82	138	138	115	2,359
One	12	8	17	27	20	22	21	22	25	12	9	26	5	10	20	13	14	14	11	298
Two	4	4	7	6	4	11	6	7	3	2	–	8	–	–	6	3	–	3	2	72
Three	1	1	–	–	–	–	2	1	1	–	–	1	–	–	–	–	–	–	–	6
Four	–	–	1	–	–	–	1	–	1	–	–	–	–	–	–	–	–	–	–	3
Five	–	–	–	–	–	–	–	–	–	1	–	–	–	–	–	–	–	–	–	1
Six	–	–	–	–	–	–	–	–	–	1	–	–	–	–	–	–	–	–	–	1
No. of Sentences in Sample	193	138	158	200	200	200	182	200	172	131	103	200	42	124	200	98	152	155	128	2,740
Chi Squared	4·3	3·3	0·8	1·0	1·1	2·0	0·9	0·4	1·9	0·3	2·3	1·3	–	3·3	0·1	0·2	2·7	1·1	1·5	
Degrees of Freedom	2	2	2	2	2	2	2	2	2	2	1	2	1	1	2	1	1	1	1	

Chi Squared = 24·2   Degrees of Freedom = 25

TABLE 42

The Occurrence of "En" in the Works of DEMOSTHENES

Works

No. of Occurrences of "En"	1	2	3	4	5	6	7	8	9	10	13	14	15	18	19	20	21	22	23	24
No "En"	85	91	104	146	66	91	91	133	128	128	102	124	94	131	134	131	133	138	132	131
One	5	9	13	12	6	8	26	23	19	20	12	5	15	19	15	17	16	12	16	17
Two	1	2	1	2	–	–	4	5	3	2	2	–	1	–	1	2	1	–	2	2
No. of Sentences in Sample	91	102	118	160	72	99	121	161	150	150	116	129	110	150	150	150	150	150	150	150

No. of Occurrences of "En"	25	27	29	30	33	34	35	36	37	39	40	42	43	44	45	47	48	49	50	52
No "En"	127	144	136	109	113	115	116	140	135	134	137	91	130	130	134	125	135	119	128	100
One	23	6	14	8	14	29	27	10	14	4	13	21	19	18	16	25	13	28	19	4
Two	–	–	–	–	–	5	1	–	1	–	–	–	1	2	–	–	2	3	–	1
Four	–	–	–	–	–	1	–	–	–	–	–	–	–	–	–	–	–	–	–	–
No. of Sentences in Sample	150	150	150	117	127	150	144	150	150	138	150	112	150	150	150	150	150	150	150	105

No. of Occurrences of "En"	53	54	55	56	57	58	59	60	61
No "En"	85	137	98	134	129	130	134	107	131
One	12	13	5	15	19	20	14	19	18
Two	3	–	2	1	2	–	2	1	1
No. of Sentences in Sample	100	150	105	150	150	150	150	127	150

For the Accepted Works: Chi Squared = 7·8   Degrees of Freedom = 26

TABLE 43

The Occurrence of "Autos" in Sentences in the History of HERODOTUS

No. of Occurrences of "Autos"	Book 1	2	3	4	5	6	7	8	9	Total
No "Autos"	165	162	146	157	159	159	169	154	169	1,440
One	33	30	49	38	32	35	27	38	26	308
Two	2	7	5	5	9	6	4	8	5	51
Three	–	1	–	–	–	–	–	–	–	1
No. of Sentences in Sample	200	200	200	200	200	200	200	200	200	1,800

Chi Squared = 16·7   Degrees of Freedom = 16

TABLE 44

The Occurrence of "Autos" in Sentences in the History of THUCYDIDES

No. of Occurrences of "Autos"	Books 1	2	3	4	5	6	7	8	Total
No "Autos"	132	124	128	121	125	126	128	103	987
One	51	58	54	63	54	54	57	76	467
Two	15	16	12	12	16	17	11	15	114
Three	2	1	6	4	4	3	3	6	29
Four	–	1	–	–	1	–	–	–	3
No. of Sentences in Sample	200	200	200	200	200	200	200	200	1,600

Chi Squared = 14·1   Degrees of Freedom = 14

TABLE 45

The Occurrence of "Autos" in Sentences in the Works of ISOCRATES

No. of Occurrences of "Autos"	Works 1	2	3	4	5	6	7	8	9	10	11	12	13	14	15	16	17	18	19
No "Autos"	178	100	104	125	134	134	126	142	109	73	61	123	22	80	135	55	96	100	69
One	13	34	47	61	50	51	50	42	48	40	32	56	14	39	52	33	40	44	41
Two	2	2	6	7	11	7	6	13	10	16	8	10	6	5	11	9	11	8	12
Three	–	2	1	7	5	6	–	2	3	1	1	7	–	–	2	2	4	1	5
Four	–	–	–	–	–	1	–	1	–	–	–	1	–	–	–	–	1	2	1
Five	–	–	–	–	–	1	–	–	1	–	1	1	–	–	–	–	–	–	–
Six	–	–	–	–	–	–	–	–	–	–	–	2	–	–	–	–	–	–	–
Seven	–	–	–	–	–	–	–	–	1	–	–	–	–	–	–	–	–	–	–
No. of Sentences in Sample	193	138	158	200	200	200	182	200	172	130	103	200	42	124	200	99	152	155	128

Chi Squared = 42·2   Degrees of Freedom = 32

TABLE 46

The Occurrence of "Autos" in Small Samples from the Works of DEMOSTHENES

No. of Occurrences of "Autos"	Work																
	1	2	3	4	5	6	7	8	9	10	13	14	15	18	19	20	21
No "Autos"	–	71	97	134	61	79	85	126	114	124	99	90	76	122	122	114	109
One	–	24	18	28	10	18	33	31	33	25	14	32	25	27	26	32	41
Two	–	7	3	1	1	2	3	4	3	1	3	5	8	–	2	4	–
Three	–	–	–	1	–	–	–	–	–	–	–	2	1	1	–	–	–
No. of Sentences in Sample	150	102	118	164	72	99	121	161	150	150	116	129	110	150	150	150	150
Chi Squared	1·3	1·8	2·2	2·8	–	–	1·7	0·4	0·1	3·5	5·3	2·3	2·4	0·7	0·7	0·1	0·7
	22	23	24	25	27	29	30	33	34	35	36	37	39	40	42	43	44
No "Autos"	120	119	121	120	88	110	73	82	102	103	124	110	113	90	94	110	111
One	27	26	26	29	57	38	41	42	43	37	22	38	22	51	17	35	35
Two	3	4	3	1	5	2	3	3	5	4	4	2	1	9	1	5	4
Three	–	1	–	–	–	–	–	–	–	–	–	–	2	–	–	–	–
No. of Sentences in Sample	150	150	150	150	150	150	117	127	150	144	150	150	138	150	112	150	150
Chi Squared	1·3	0·5	1·0	1·3	23·1	0·1	10·8	7·6	4·6	1·2	3·5	0·4	2·5	20·5	3·1	0·7	0·7
			45	47	48	49	50	52	53	54	55	56	57	58	59	60	61
No "Autos"			98	107	110	103	99	60	53	106	84	100	119	97	67	101	132
One			46	34	38	40	41	34	33	33	20	42	29	46	51	24	17
Two			6	8	2	5	8	9	12	1	1	7	2	6	26	2	1
Three			–	1	–	2	2	2	2	–	–	1	–	1	4	–	–
Four			–	–	–	–	–	–	–	–	–	–	–	–	2	–	–
No. of Sentences in Sample			150	150	150	150	150	105	100	140	105	150	150	150	150	127	150
Chi Squared			8·7	1·4	0·7	3·8	7·3	19·3	27·1	0·1	0·8	6·3	0·5	9·5	7·8	0·8	12·1

TABLE 47

The Occurrence of "Einai" in Sentences in the Works of HERODOTUS

No. of Occurrences of "Einai"	Books 1	2	3	4	5	6	7	8	9	Total
No "Einai"	147	107	142	144	140	156	142	143	146	1,267
One	47	65	44	45	49	36	46	48	44	424
Two	6	22	13	10	8	6	11	8	5	89
Three	–	4	1	–	3	2	–	1	4	15
Four	–	1	–	1	–	–	1	–	1	4
Five	–	1	–	–	–	–	–	–	–	1
No. of Sentences in Sample	200	200	200	200	200	200	200	200	200	1,800

For eight samples, Sample Two excluded: Chi squared $=$ 6·4; degrees of freedom $=$ 14

For Sample Two   : Chi squared $=$ 40·8; degrees of freedom $=$ 2

TABLE 48

The Occurrence of "Einai" in Sentences in the Works of THUCYDIDES

No. of Occurrences of "Einai"	Books 1	2	3	4	5	6	7	8	Total
No "Einai"	126	129	141	131	129	141	147	147	1,091
One	56	58	45	55	57	45	42	46	404
Two	16	8	12	9	11	12	9	5	82
Three	2	2	2	2	3	2	2	1	16
Four	–	2	–	3	–	–	–	–	5
Five	–	–	–	–	–	–	–	1	1
Six	–	1	–	–	–	–	–	–	1
No. of Sentences in Sample	200	200	200	200	200	200	200	200	1,600

Chi Squared = 15·0   Degrees of Freedom = 14

TABLE 49

The Occurrence of "Einai" in Sentences in the Works of ISOCRATES

No. of Occurrences of "Einai"	Works																		Total
	1	2	3	4	5	6	7	8	9	10	11	12	14	15	16	17	18	19	
No "Einai"	159	94	102	130	146	132	129	139	113	87	70	145	83	115	75	110	111	94	1,874
One	31	36	48	55	43	56	42	45	48	31	27	45	36	68	17	36	38	25	696
Two	2	6	8	11	8	10	10	14	11	8	5	8	4	16	5	5	5	9	143
Three	1	1	–	2	3	2	1	2	–	4	1	1	1	1	1	1	1	–	23
Five	–	–	–	2	–	–	–	–	–	1	–	1	–	–	–	–	–	–	4
No. of Sentences in Sample	193	137	158	200	200	200	182	200	172	131	103	200	124	200	98	152	155	128	2,740

Chi Squared = 28·5   Degrees of Freedom = 32

TABLE 50

The Occurrence of "Einai" in Small Samples from DEMOSTHENES

No. of Occurrences of "Einai"	Works 2	3	4	6	7	8	9	10	13	14	15	18	19	20	21	22
No "Einai"	67	81	110	67	54	111	94	101	74	83	76	103	110	79	97	90
One	31	34	46	31	56	46	52	41	37	37	25	40	35	60	45	50
Two	4	3	8	1	10	2	3	8	5	9	8	7	5	10	6	10
Three	–	–	–	–	1	2	1	–	–	–	1	–	–	1	1	–
Four	–	–	–	–	–	–	–	–	–	–	–	–	–	–	–	–
No. of Sentences in Sample	102	118	164	99	121	161	150	150	116	129	110	150	150	150	150	150

No. of Occurrences of "Einai"	23	24	25	27	29	30	33	34	35	36	37	39	40	42	43	44
No "Einai"	87	98	98	113	103	81	83	106	74	94	95	66	103	82	58	76
One	53	43	48	34	39	31	37	38	54	44	47	59	41	25	70	56
Two	10	8	4	2	8	4	6	6	15	9	8	11	6	5	20	18
Three	–	1	–	1	–	1	1	–	1	3	–	2	–	–	1	–
Four	–	–	–	–	–	–	–	–	–	–	–	–	–	–	1	–
No. of Sentences in Sample	150	150	150	150	150	117	127	150	144	150	150	138	150	112	150	150

No. of Occurrences of "Einai"	45	47	48	49	50	52	53	54	55	56	57	58	59	60	61
No "Einai"	85	101	97	114	113	67	55	94	79	111	84	92	84	80	109
One	50	43	45	33	31	33	41	50	23	37	50	47	57	43	34
Two	13	5	8	3	5	5	4	5	3	2	15	10	9	4	6
Three	1	1	–	–	1	–	–	1	–	–	1	1	–	–	1
Four	1	–	–	–	–	–	–	–	–	–	–	–	–	–	–
No. of Sentences in Sample	150	150	150	150	150	105	100	150	105	150	150	150	150	127	150

o

TABLE 51

The Sentence Length Distributions of the PAULINE CORPUS—A.

Number of Sentences in the Epistles

No. of Words in Sentence	Romans					I Cor.						II Cor.			
	1	2	3	4	Total	1	2	3	4	Remainder	Total	1	2	3	Total
1—5	34	30	32	14	110	31	28	29	30	7	125	9	18	29	56
6—10	46	52	62	54	214	48	74	55	62	14	253	23	33	47	103
11—15	21	25	26	41	113	34	28	42	29	5	138	24	21	18	63
16—20	9	21	16	11	57	20	13	10	16	1	60	16	17	16	49
21—25	21	11	6	4	42	7	2	8	10	–	27	14	11	7	32
26—30	6	4	5	–	15	5	1	2	1	–	9	9	5	5	19
31—35	3	3	1	3	10	2	2	2	2	1	9	3	1	1	5
36—40	4	1	–	1	6	1	–	–	–	–	1	1	–	1	1
41—45	2	1	1	1	5	1	1	–	–	–	2	2	1	1	4
46—50	2	2	1	1	6	–	1	2	–	–	3	–	–	–	–
51—55	–	–	–	1	1	–	–	–	–	–	–	–	–	1	1
56—60	1	–	–	–	1	1	–	–	–	–	1	–	–	–	–
61—65	1	–	–	–	1	–	–	–	–	–	–	–	1	–	1
66—70	–	–	–	–	–	–	–	–	–	–	–	–	–	–	1
No. of Sentences	150	150	150	131	581	150	150	150	150	28	628	100	108	126	334

The Sentence Length Distributions of the PAULINE CORPUS—A (Contd.)

Number of Sentences in the Epistles

No. of Words in Sentence	Gal.	Eph.	Phil.	Col.	I Thess.	II Thess.	I Tim.	II Tim.	Titus	Phile-mon	A	Hebrews B	R	T
1—5	26	9	9	6	4	3	14	19	7	1	7	11	4	22
6—10	62	10	26	17	23	8	27	17	5	8	30	51	7	88
11—15	50	24	31	18	17	8	26	23	8	4	45	41	3	89
16—20	19	14	15	13	12	7	20	16	7	5	22	20	–	42
21—25	12	10	5	8	9	3	10	3	3	–	16	9	–	25
26—30	7	6	4	7	3	5	2	3	2	2	5	11	–	16
31—35	1	6	4	7	6	1	2	6	1	1	12	2	–	14
36—40	3	7	3	3	2	3	2	–	–	–	5	1	–	6
41—45	–	3	2	1	–	–	1	1	1	–	4	1	1	6
46—50	–	2	2	1	4	2	2	–	1	1	2	2	–	4
51—55	–	1	1	–	–	–	–	–	1	–	–	1	–	1
56—60	1	1	–	1	–	–	1	–	1	–	1	–	–	1
61—65	–	1	–	–	–	–	–	–	–	–	1	–	–	1
66—70	–	3	–	–	–	–	–	–	–	–	–	–	–	–
71—75	–	1	–	1	1	1	–	1	–	–	–	–	–	–
76—80	–	–	–	–	–	–	–	–	–	–	–	–	–	–
81—85	–	1	–	–	–	–	–	–	–	–	–	–	–	–
139	–	1	–	–	–	–	–	–	–	–	–	–	–	–
No. of Sentences	181	100	102	83	81	41	107	89	37	22	150	150	15	315

TABLE 51 (Contd.)

The Sentence Length Distributions of the PAULINE CORPUS—B

Epistle	Mean	Standard Error	Median	Standard Error	First Quartile	Standard Error	Third Quartile	Standard Error	Ninth Decile	Standard Error
ROMANS										
1	14·6	0·98	9·5	0·67	5·38	0·58	20·6	1·26	28·3	3·06
2	12·3	0·73	9·3	0·59	5·72	0·51	16·3	1·26	23·2	1·67
3	10·8	0·62	8·5	0·49	5·44	0·43	13·6	1·02	19·7	1·15
4	12·1	0·72	9·8	0·53	6·74	0·46	13·7	0·60	19·1	1·56
Total	12·30	0·39	9·2	0·28	5·82	0·24	14·9	0·46	23·4	0·86
I CORINTHIANS										
1	11·9	0·69	9·6	0·64	5·7	0·55	14·9	0·78	21·4	2·6
2	10·0	0·56	8·2	0·41	5·6	0·36	11·9	0·95	16·9	1·4
3	11·0	0·61	9·2	0·56	5·8	0·48	13·4	0·63	19·5	3·7
4	10·5	0·52	8·6	0·49	5·6	0·43	13·5	0·92	19·4	1·2
Total	10·8	0·29	8·7	0·25	5·6	0·21	13·4	0·39	19·1	0·63
II CORINTHIANS										
1	13·5	0·9	13·8	1·0	8·5	1·1	21·0	1·5	27·2	1·7
2	13·1	0·9	10·7	1·2	6·4	0·7	19·1	2·0	23·7	1·4
3	12·7	0·8	8·6	0·6	5·3	0·5	15·2	1·5	22·4	2·4
Total	13·1	0·5	10·6	0·7	6·3	0·4	17·9	0·8	24·6	0·9
GALATIANS	12·4	0·6	10·3	0·67	6·6	0·47	15·0	0·58	22·6	1·7
EPHESIANS	24·3	2·07	17·5	1·8	11·3	0·9	31·7	3·6	47·5	7·5
PHILIPPIANS	15·9	1·07	12·6	0·81	9·9	0·84	18·50	1·46	32·3	2·3
COLOSSIANS	19·0	1·42	20·1	1·75	9·3	1·16	29·5	2·50	41·2	4·6
I THESSALONIANS	18·1	1·34	14·0	1·32	8·53	0·85	22·6	2·17	34·1	2·3
I TIMOTHY	14·8	0·99	12·40	0·99	7·36	0·83	18·3	1·12	24·7	1·6
II TIMOTHY	14·0	1·12	11·9	1·03	6·0	1·20	17·4	1·28	28·5	4·7
HEBREWS										
1	18·2	0·92	14·2	0·68	10·1	0·63	21·3	0·88	34·2	1·5
2	14·3	0·72	11·6	0·75	7·6	0·55	17·4	1·4	26·4	1·7
Total	15·9	0·63	12·7	0·50	8·2	0·44	19·4	0·95	30·5	1·9

TABLE 52

The Occurrence of "Kai" in the PAULINE EPISTLES—A
The Proportion of "Kai" in the Epistles

Epistle	Occurrences of "Kai"	No. of Occurrences of all Words	Proportion of "Kai" in Epistle
Romans	274	7,106	0·0386
I Corinthians	282	6,814	0·0414
II Corinthians	197	4,472	0·0441
Galatians	72	2,233	0·0322
Ephesians	137	2,415	0·0567
Philippians	107	1,630	0·0656
Colossians	99	1,579	0·0627
I Thessalonians	99	1,471	0·0673
II Thessalonians	49	822	0·0596
I Timothy	92	1,591	0·0578
II Timothy	68	1,238	0·0549
Titus	36	657	0·056
Philemon	17	336	0·05
Hebrews	255	4,951	0·0516

For the Four Major Epistles
Romans — Galatians

Chi Squared $= 6·0$

Degrees of Freedom $= 3$

TABLE 52 (Contd.)

The Occurrence of "Kai" in Sentences—B

No. of "Kais" in Sentence	Ro.	I Cor.	II Cor.	Gal.	Eph.	Phil.	Col.	I Thes.	I Tim.	II Tim.	Hebrews
No "Kai"	385	425	198	128	33	54	26	35	49	46	158
One	145	152	93	42	30	27	31	21	39	28	96
Two	34	35	29	5	22	19	18	8	10	11	38
Three or more	17	16	14	6	15	12	8	17	9	4	23
Total	581	628	334	181	100	102	83	81	107	89	315

TABLE 52 (Contd.)

The Occurrence of "Kai" in Small Samples—C

No. of "Kais" in Sample	Romans	Corinthians I	Galatians	Total	Poisson Expectation
		Number of Samples in			
No "Kai"	160	162	62	384	361
One	136	102	32	270	289
Two	39	56	12	107	115
Three	17	16	4	37	38
Four	–	–	1	1	
Five	1	–	–	1	
Six	–	1	–	1	
Mean	0·77	0·81	0·65	0·770	Chi Squared = 3·5
Standard Error of Mean	0·05	0·05	0·09	0·032	Degrees of Freedom = 2
Variance	0·75	0·93	0·77	0·839	

TABLE 52 (Contd.)

The Occurrences of "Kai" in Sentences—D

No. of Occurrences of "Kai" in Sentence	I Corinthians						II Corinthians				Romans				
	1	2	3	4	5	Total	1	2	3	Total	1	2	3	4	Total
No "Kai"	103	106	100	96	20	425	52	60	86	198	90	114	107	74	385
One	31	34	39	43	5	152	37	29	27	93	36	32	34	43	145
Two	11	6	7	9	2	35	7	13	9	29	19	2	6	7	34
Three	3	2	2	2	–	9	3	5	3	11	2	1	1	6	10
Four	1	–	1	–	1	3	1	–	1	2	2	–	2	1	5
Five	–	2	1	–	–	3	–	1	–	1	1	–	–	–	1
Six	1	–	–	–	–	1	–	–	–	–	–	1	–	–	1
No. of Sentences in Sample	150	150	150	150	28	628	100	108	126	334	150	150	150	131	581

TABLE 53

The Occurrences of "De" in the PAULINE EPISTLES—A

The Occurrence of "De" as Second or Third Word in a Sentence

Sample	Sentences with "De" as 2nd or 3rd Word	Total No. of Sentences in Sample	Proportion of Sentences with "De" as 2nd or 3rd Word	Standard Error of Proportion
ROMANS				
1	25	150	0·167	
2	34	150	0·227	
3	21	150	0·140	
4	20	131	0·153	
Total	100	581	0·172	0·016
I CORINTHIANS				
1	25	150	0·167	
2	40	150	0·267	
3	33	150	0·220	
4	41	150	0·273	
5	7	28	0·250	
Total	146	628	0·232	0·017
II CORINTHIANS				
1	23	100	0·230	
2	18	108	0·167	
3	15	126	0·119	
Total	56	334	0·168	0·020
GALATIANS	46	181	0·254	0·032
EPHESIANS	11	100	0·110	0·031
PHILIPPIANS	16	102	0·157	0·036
COLOSSIANS	3	83	0·036	0·020
I THESSALONIANS	13	81	0·160	0·041
I TIMOTHY	24	107	0·224	0·040
II TIMOTHY	17	89	0·191	0·042
HEBREWS	47	315	0·149	0·020

TABLE 53 (Contd.)

The Occurrence of "De" in Later Position in Sentence—B

No. of "De" in Sentences	Rom.	I Cor.	II Cor.	Gal.	Eph.	Phil.	Col.	I Thes.	I Tim.	II Tim.	Heb.
One	36	42	18	12	6	9	2	1	6	5	20
Two	4	2	–	–	–	1	–	–	–	1	1
Three	1	4	–	–	1	–	–	–	–	–	–

TABLE 54

The Occurrence of Common Words in Sentences in THE PAULINE EPISTLES

No. of Words in Sentence	Rom.	I Cor.	II Cor.	Gal.	Eph.	Phil.	Col.	I Thess.	I Tim.	II Tim.	Heb.
"En"											
No "En"	449	504	232	147	46	56	33	46	78	61	263
One	104	90	71	26	25	30	24	23	20	21	41
Two	18	26	21	8	11	11	19	4	7	5	9
Three	9	6	3	—	9	3	3	7	2	2	2
Four	1	1	2	—	4	1	3	—	—	—	—
Five	—	1	1	—	2	—	1	—	—	—	—
Six	—	—	2	—	1	—	—	—	—	—	—
Seven	—	—	—	—	1	—	—	—	—	—	—
Eight	—	—	1	—	1	—	—	—	—	—	—
Nineteen	—	—	1	—	—	—	—	—	—	—	—
"Autos"											
No "Autos"	472	562	288	160	66	80	49	60	101	76	213
One	77	57	43	18	20	15	22	17	6	10	76
Two	27	6	1	2	6	4	9	2	—	3	21
Three	4	3	2	1	2	1	—	1	—	—	5
Four	1	—	—	—	4	1	—	—	—	—	—
Five	—	—	—	—	2	—	—	—	—	—	—
Seven	—	—	—	—	1	—	1	—	—	—	—
"Einai"											
No "Einai"	486	492	277	139	61	86	57	68	76	72	271
One	89	114	52	30	33	13	22	12	30	16	41
Two	3	19	5	12	5	2	2	—	1	1	2
Three	2	3	—	—	2	—	—	—	—	—	1
Four	1	—	—	—	—	—	—	—	—	—	—

INDEX